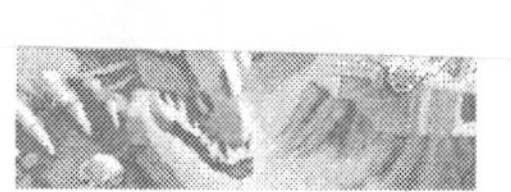

Of The Unexpected

Edited by Steve Twelvetree

Disclaimer

Young Writers has maintained every effort
to publish stories that will not cause offence.

Any stories, events or activities relating to individuals
should be read as fictional pieces and not construed
as real-life character portrayal.

First published in Great Britain in 2005 by:
Young Writers
Remus House
Coltsfoot Drive
Peterborough
PE2 9JX
Telephone: 01733 890066
Website: www.youngwriters.co.uk

SB ISBN 1 84602 325 4

Foreword

Young Writers was established in 1991 and has been passionately devoted to the promotion of reading and writing in children and young adults ever since. The quest continues today. *Young Writers* remains as committed to engendering the fostering of burgeoning poetic and literary talent as ever.

This year, *Young Writers* are happy to present a dynamic and entertaining new selection of the best creative writing from a talented and diverse cross section of some of the most accomplished secondary school writers around. Entrants were presented with four inspirational and challenging themes.

'Myths And Legends' gave pupils the opportunity to adapt long-established tales from mythology (whether Greek, Roman, Arthurian or more conventional eg The Loch Ness Monster) to their own style.

'A Day In The Life Of ...' offered pupils the chance to depict twenty-four hours in the lives of literally anyone they could imagine. A hugely imaginative wealth of entries were received encompassing days in the lives of everyone from the top media celebrities to historical figures like Henry VIII or a typical soldier from the First World War.

Finally 'Short Stories', in contrast, offered no limit other than the author's own imagination while 'Hold The Front Page' provided the ideal opportunity to challenge the entrants' journalistic skills, asking them to provide a newspaper or magazine article on any subject of their choice.

T.A.L.E.S. Of The Unexpected is ultimately a collection we feel sure you will love, featuring as it does the work of the best young authors writing today.

Contents

The Creative Writing

A Day In The Life Of My Dog

The first thing she does is get up in the morning in my mum's room. She runs all the way down the stairs for a drink of water. Then she waits for me to get out of bed because she wants me to take her for a walk.

After she has been for a walk she has her food. After that she goes to bed for a rest. When I come home from school she goes for a walk to the shop for some treats.

When we get home she eats a few of her treats. Then she goes in the back garden to play with her ball, then she play fights with me and after that she goes in the front room to sit in the sun or in front of the fire.

She then falls asleep again. When she wakes up she plays with her teddy and then goes up the stairs into my mum's room to sleep.

Thomas Kirton (14)

A Perfect Place

(An extract)

'The Controllers are the enemy ... never allow us to do what we want to ... ' Snatches of the ranting man's speech drifted across the churned up mud. Izzie turned, her dirty blonde hair tucked firmly behind her ear. The shouting man stood on a rock in the centre of the slum. His unshaven face contorted in a sneer as he raved on, his arms flying about him creating the impression of a madman. Izzie knew what he was saying, knew what he was feeling. Their lives were miserable, as a commoner you had little food, almost no money and no freedom. Well, until you committed a crime, then they banished you to the wasteland. 'They' were the Controllers, the name said it all, they controlled anyone who was lower than them in the system. In other words, everyone.

But he was preaching to the converted here, and at the risk of doing himself more harm than good. The Guardians would be on their way and they hated rule breakers and 'wrongdoers'. They would punish him severely for rebelling.

Izzie certainly didn't want to see his punishment, she'd heard way too many stories. Just before she turned her head for home, something bright caught her eye, she glanced at the point where the light met the coolness of the shadows. A group of five cloaked figures were gliding out of the shadows, the burning afternoon sun reflecting off their white garments; white meaning good, pure, neutral. The Guardians were none of these, their violent manner was used to subdue 'wrongdoers', people who rebelled against the System. The System was to be obeyed at all costs, anyone found in violation of one of the many laws faced a penalty. Your penalty depended on who you were and whether the Guardians were in a good mood, so far that hadn't ever happened.

The first Guardian to reach the man pulled its hood down to reveal a scarred face. Izzie tried to look away but her eyes were drawn to the sockets where the creature's eyes should have been. A thin semi-transparent layer of skin had grown across the empty holes, black hollows in their mangled faces. The man's voice faltered and he fell silent, his eyes transfixed on the Guardian's face as it loomed towards him. Izzie willed him to run, even if he'd thought of running, he couldn't have moved a muscle. He was frozen stiff by fear. A second Guardian glided up, lowering its hood as it came closer to the man.

The commoners who had been listening to his speech, who had been jeering and shouting with him, had since scattered, desperate to get into their mouldering shacks, away from the Guardians.

Izzie couldn't pull away, just like the doomed man, she was frozen to the spot, forced, against her will to watch. By now the other three Guardians had reached the shivering man, they formed a circle and began to chant. Izzie didn't want to see this, didn't want to hear this, didn't want to be here. But, just as the man in front of her was frozen, so too was she. The power of movement having long been stolen from her cold body ...

Katie Dorey (15)

A Soldier's Life In The War

Monday 26th November 1914

The life of us is painful - we get threatened, we have dirty water and no food. It's been raining for five days, we're drenched. Ten people have died of hunger and six people have been shot for running away. We're all scared to death that we'll get pummelled with machine-gun bullets when we go over.

Tuesday 27th November 1914

So far it's stopped raining and it is freezing instead. We all got telegrams from our families except me. I'm all alone, lots of my friends are dead and I think I will be too. But if I survive I'm one of the lucky ones. But I sure am glad I'm not the only one left, there's eight of us left including me - nine. I've been starving and thirsty for days. In five days we go over the top and I hope I live to see the next day of my life.

Wednesday 28th November 1914

Today we saw the Kaiser's men spying on us in their trench with a periscope. After a while the Germans started to stand ready for us to go over the top, but we didn't because our orders suddenly changed so we survive one more day to sit and wait for the next day's orders. It could be my final day in the English Vs German war.

Thursday 29th November 1914

They started throwing over grenades today. Twenty men were blown to pieces; I even found a hand in my dugout although everyone found something of someone. I know we are all going to die one day but I think it could be tomorrow, the last day of November.

Friday 30th November 1914

The grenades are coming over every second now, argh! A grenade went off right next to me. I'm lucky. Uh-oh, the whistle. *Oh God help me!* Well I hope I survive over the top. I really hope so because I think I probably won't. I'm truly terrified.

Monday 1st December 1914

I'm in hospital. I got hit by a bullet in my shoulder. I survived. Somebody picked me up and dragged me to a trench. Don't know who he was.

Friday 24th December 1914

Today we played a football match with the Germans. It was fun. We won but right after we went back to killing again. I think that's strange because one minute we're happy and then we're not.

Thursday 11th November 1918

The war's over now. The leaders have signed a truce, we won. I'm glad it's over. I'm back with my family and friends, they all were happy to see me and I was to see them. They were all asking me what happened but I could never tell them the truth.

In the war millions died and some people are still alive today and we will always remember the soldiers that never made it home.

Zac Rigby

James And The Dragon

'Tomo, how do you feel about the dragon coming to eat our sheep?' James texted his best pal.

James got a text back: 'I don't like the dragon, you know how much I like lamb chops, I haven't any lately!'

James chuckled, he always thought Tomo was a joker. Then he had a thought, *what will the dragon eat when the sheep are gone?*

Time flew. Every day the same thing happened, they gave the dragon two sheep. The people did what they planned and that was it. But one day they realised that tomorrow they would have no sheep. Everyone panicked when they saw the flyers the mayor put up.

It read: 'We have no sheep. Tomorrow we shall weep. When the dragon is awake, some people he will bake. In alphabetical order, people will be sacrificed'.

Tomo's last name was Smith so he had a while to live, but James' last name was Crouch. He didn't have long ...

People were sacrificed every single day, even the mayor's daughter. The mayor protested and was given eight days. The mayor bought her mobile phones, computers, MP3s and took her everywhere, but now she's gone.

Tomo and James spent a lot of time with each other, with only a few days left until James' demise.

Eventually James was sent out to the dragon - huge with wings and hard green scales! Nobody knew James had brought a gun! He took it out and had three shots. One shot hit it in the mouth. James returned with the dragon (dead): a hero.

Patrick Harrison (11)

Batboy

Never underestimate your abilities, never doubt yourself, never misuse your skills because anything can happen, no matter who you are or where you come from.

The darkness and gloom of the night, scared people into their houses. Except one, who had no one and nowhere to go. The young child Billy was an orphan that was lost but his bravery kept him alive in the suburbs of New York City. After years of searching for his parents he had come to believe that he had no parents, but he knew they would not leave him and something must have happened to them leaving him destined to find the truth.

All of a sudden Billy ran and ran as he was being chased by bats. Nothing could stop them, you could see the horror in the young boy's eyes. When suddenly he fell, the bats amazingly stopped and scurried backwards. Billy began to feel a glow, a glow of strength and power.

The night went on and Billy may not have realised it but inside him a new power had evolved in him.

After days and nights the weather began to improve, giving him the chance to reveal himself to the world.

Without realising, he could sense trouble, giving him the ability to scare people and retrieve their goods.

With his new skills to track enemies and save the innocent he was able to find out what was behind his parents disappearing, as *Batboy* could now track back in time for his descendants.

Zafir Manji (14)
Brooke Weston City Technology College, Corby

Fate

The room is tense. You can feel the anger rising from the worried council. The beast is lying there, motionless. As it stays, the onlookers grow in fear. The being has terrorised your families. It is now your turn to decide its fate. As the meeting unfolds it seems inevitable that the beast should die.

During the meeting the silence is unbearable. You can feel the blood pumping through every part of your body. An old man hobbles in. You have asked him to come in for a talk. He gives you the talk, he nervously says, 'The vampire is a terrible creature. Thought to be extinct years ago. There is only one real way to kill a vampire. It must be a wooden stake through the heart. If it is left how it is, it will regenerate energy through the fear created. Move as quickly as you can. Don't be scared.' The man stumbles out and you watch him disappear into the darkness.

You walk out and lock the only way out. The door. There is one key - it is round your neck. The vampire is inside and nothing more. The council watch and leave you. It is up to you now.

You carve a stake. A perfect specimen. Now, it's your job to kill the vampire. Armed with a stake you open the door. It's not inside. You turn. The vampire stares into your eyes. The teeth are shining in the moonlight.

Elliot Thurland (14)
Brooke Weston City Technology College, Corby

The Murder

The rain battered down upon the thick glass of the large manor, thunder clapped like cymbals and the lightning flashed threateningly. A woman walked from a room in the manor. As the door closed an inhuman sound was reverberating from the cellar, a loud clunk, followed by a low, painful groan. The woman's heart began to race, sweat beads soaked her face and she began to shake.

'H . . . hello?' she trembled. The groaning stopped. 'Is anyone there? Are you alright?'

Clunk.

'Are you alright?' she repeated.

Clunk.

The sound was now at an ear-splitting level, the woman began to step slowly backwards as the cellar door creaked open. A yellow, scabbed hand curled around the side of the door, a grunt and then a large metallic foot stepped out, followed by a grotesque, ugly being. He was at least 7 foot tall, his skin was yellowing and scarred. Ugly great scabs were invading his huge, crooked hands. His hair was a dark, black helmet upon his square-jawed face. His eyes were a dark midnight-black, which were cold and unshining. The mouth was barely a stitch across his chin and emitted nought but a groan.

The monster stared wickedly at the woman and held out a grim hand. The only sound was Elizabeth's breathing and the occasional clap of thunder before the monster uttered two words in his criminally evil voice.

'Kill you!'

The monster stepped forwards and placed a hand around Elizabeth's neck.

A blood-curdling scream. *Thud*. Silence.

Nichelle Gibney (14)
Brooke Weston City Technology College, Corby

The Disappearance

Katy had just moved school, she was so nervous for her first day. Katy was a bright girl, she had straight As all through her last school.

On her way to school, she noticed posters on lamp posts and on walls. They said, *Girl Disappeared*. Of course Katy had no idea who this girl was, but after that day she started to get visions of her, it was as if she knew her, but Katy was unable to put a name to her face.

Weeks went by and Katy was trying to look over disappearance lists to see who she was but no one knew her. There was no record of her, so she left it, put all her findings - which were useless, in a drawer. From there on, when she woke up that drawer was also open, even if it was locked! At first Katy thought it was her brother Tommy, but as days went by, she began to wonder if she'd missed something.

So she pulled all of the newspaper clippings and statements out. As she was rummaging through she found a picture of the girl, it looked just like her.

At this point Katy was shocked, speechless she read the caption beneath the picture. It said, 'Teenage girl disappeared, aged 15' which was how old Katy was. She tried to put two and two together but all she could come up with was that the girl was her.

Becki Potter (14)
Brooke Weston City Technology College, Corby

The Animal Within

I sprinted through the foreboding woods. I didn't know where I was going but I knew, if I slowed, down it would catch up with me, then and hopefully only then, my fate would be decided. I knew I shouldn't have come here, but yet again my curiosity had got the better of me.

I had entered the woods with my friend Ryan, but when we heard it, we ran, I don't know where Ryan is now.

I hurdled over the roots of the giant oak trees and dived under thorn bushes, being torn apart and stumbling over the undergrowth I stopped and sat down, leaning against a tree panting. It was silent, the blood rushing through my ears sounded like a wall of water crashing down, my heart pounding louder than a bass drum. I slouched against the tree, feeling weak and defenceless.

I kept listening, waiting, trying to hear it. There was a rustle in the bushes. I peered around the tree to see what it was. The bush shook again. *Just a rabbit*, I thought. How wrong I was. *'Argh!'*

Robert Cassie (13)
Brooke Weston City Technology College, Corby

Untitled

The most amazing village in the land was inhabited by a very gracious ghost. The village was in harmony, it was like a make-believe heaven.

But one day it would all begin to change. Erik the evil ghost came to town. He was welcomed by Gerald the good ghost. It went seriously sour when burglaries and fires were set off. A dark, gloomy cloud swarmed over the village. The wicked witch flew like an eagle into the village! The question was asked who did it? Each of the villagers were frightened of speaking out. Erik pointed the finger at Gerald. So Gerald was removed indefinitely from the village.

Gerald, in his anger surrounded the village cutting off all supplies. The people were living in poverty, they didn't have enough water, heat or food.

For days the wise men pondered over what to do. They finally realised they needed to contact the witch.

In the middle of a mist of spirit they sent up many flares. Time and time again they had no reply, finally they contacted the witch. She realised they were in trouble. The witch found a gap in the spirit and entered the village. The witch returned the ghost to the village in turn suspending Erik.

Erik was sent away again, searching for a new village to haunt. Gerald was welcomed back into the village. Everything was returned to normal but from that day, on the darkest night, Erik returns causing havoc once again!

Ben Johnson (14)
Brooke Weston City Technology College, Corby

A Day In The Life Of £10

I was happy in the sparkling bank piled high with friends. There were lots of us there. I was new and pristine and ironed flat. It was great, but then disaster struck because I didn't want to leave. I was moved by a shabby man's hands. I was terrified about what trouble I would cause. Immediately I heard him say he wanted drugs so he swapped me for a little packet. I was taken down to the chemist and he swapped it for a bottle that was brown and I could make out on the bottle it said 'cough medicine'. Next thing I knew was that someone opened up the dark till drawer and gave me to a small, vivacious woman who put me in a purse, and she took me to her enormous tower block.

I finally thought that this was going to be my home but a few minutes later her husband took me down to the corner shop and used me to buy himself a magazine. Again I felt lonely and I missed all of my friends back at the bank.

Some kids came downstairs and opened up the till on a table in the shop and threw me on the floor - this was hell. Then they played with me outside. It was cold and also snowing and the wind was blowing me all over the place. I couldn't wait for it to end - there was no hope for me. I felt depressed and lonely. Oh no, down the drain.

John Fretwell (14)
Budehaven Community School, Bude

A Day In The Life Of A Pig On Wheels

One day I was a pig in a pigsty. My brothers and sisters didn't like me barging them about as I was very fat. My rolls wobbled about sending bedding flying around the sty. Mummy pig often told me to go on a diet, but I would ignore her and say, 'I'm just big boned'. But every day I would get bigger and bigger.

But one day I got a shock. Two wild dogs came across the farmer's field and into the yard. They said to one another, 'I can hear baby pigs. Let's go eat them and their mother.'

They ate my brothers and sisters, then my mother and turned on me. I squealed for help but no one came, not even the farmer. The dogs decided I was just fat and bone but then without warning bit off my two back legs. The only thing I could do was squeal for my life. The dogs ran off with my legs and I was left behind.

When the farmer came out to see what the noise was about he took me to the vet and I had stitches. Then the farmer took me to his workshop and made a small trolley with two wheels. This was attached by straps to my behind. *Now I'm the pig on wheels.*

Samuel Allenby Medland (14)
Budehaven Community School, Bude

Follow The Waves

'Blimmin' hell,' I shouted, 'everybody hold onto something.'

'Why?' Old man Clunk asked.

'Just get down,' I shouted to the rest of the crew on the grand ship, Mary Lou, just as a huge wave swept over us. A fork of lightning came down and struck the mast which caught fire and fell.

'Everybody off.'

'What?' they all shouted at me in unison, with looks on their faces as if I were bonkers.

'Just jump off and swim, you'll have a better chance of living than if you stay on a burning boat,' I called to them all. We all jumped off into the raging sea just as the ship blew up.

'Follow the waves.'

'What?' I asked.

'Follow the waves,' all the crew were whispering to me.

'I don't understand, what do you mean follow the waves?' I said.

Old man Clunk stepped forward. 'Just follow the waves Captain,' he said, 'just follow the waves and you'll get home safely, we'll all help you.' He pointed at the rest of the crew, they were all beginning to fade.

'Follow the waves,' they all said in unison one last time and then I woke up.

Where am I? I thought to myself. Small waves were sloshing over me and I had sand all around me. Then I remembered what had happened on the ship the night before.

The others, where are the others? I said to myself. Then I remembered the dream I had just woken up from. They must have died before they got to the shore. 'Follow the waves,' a voice inside my head was saying. I got to my feet and saw a massive sign made of sticks and stones lay on the sand. It read *Follow The Waves*. For the next few days I thought and thought and suddenly realised what follow the waves meant. I built myself a raft and just followed the waves. About 5 weeks later, I arrived home and guess what, the rest of the crew were there, alive and well.

Victoria Vincent (13)
Budehaven Community School, Bude

Follow The Waves

A long time ago on a deserted island was a young chap called Wolly Seabass. One day Wolly Seabass was taking a trip on his little red wooden boat but, all of a sudden, a giant wave came and swept him away and well, let's just say, the boat was not to be seen again. Wolly saw an island. He looked around him and saw no other island, he then realised that this island was his only hope. So he swam as quickly as his strength could take him. When he got on the island he was gasping for breath. He was breathing so hard that he thought that he was dying. Wolly knew that he wasn't going to get any help unless someone came out on a ferry or a boat and spotted him. The only food he had was the bananas on the tree on the island.

The sun was starting to go down. Wolly was starting to feel cold; the water was coming in quicker and quicker. Wolly knew he had to do something to stop himself getting swept out to sea. Wolly knew that his only hope was to get onto high land and off the sand. Wolly looked up and realised that his only hope was to climb the banana tree. So that is what he did. He tried to make himself as comfortable as he could to settle down for the cold night.

In the night Wolly heard a loud noise, like a horn on a ferry or something. He realised that a boat was coming closer and closer to the island. He knew that if he could catch the captain of the boat it would be his only chance of getting off the island. So Wolly was waving his hands in the air and started to shout help as loud as he could.

He saw what the boat was. It was a trawler. He realised that the boat was coming to get him. He kept waving his hands in the air and in the end the boat came and rescued him. Wolly was so grateful for help that Wolly asked the captain if he would help him find a new boat to replace his old one. The captain said, 'Yes I will.' In the end Wolly found a new boat which was much better than his old one. He got a boat called 'Bonzoe'. The boat was all metal and small enough for one person. Wolly was now a happy person and glad that he had made a new friend.

Donna Jasper (13)
Budehaven Community School, Bude

Waves

OK, I'm writing a story and I cannot be bothered to write 'once upon a boring time' that is *sooo* 1909 and saying 'one day not so long ago' is the same way every other author uses it so I won't bother with it.

OK, I was sitting in the garden as usual and felt this cracking sound. A sound I had never heard, well not as I know of, and this cracking sound turned into a crumbling sound. It was too late for me to do anything. OK, I lied, I had approximately 30 seconds but what could I do? Go in the shed and make it fall even faster? Just to get my bike out? No way. I was a little stunned but the same thing happened to my neighbour yesterday.

I lived in Cornwall nearly on the edge of a cliff and this shed of mine was pretty close to going over the edge. Anyway it fell into the sea, the man-eating sea, the man-eating waves of the sea, and yes everything was not saved. What a pain in the ass it was that day. I've had a new bike since then and I didn't pay for it, the insurance did.

I'm a surf chick now. It is so cool and refreshing, I seriously recommend it to all ages.

It's fun falling in the sea and I found my old bike yesterday. It needed a bit of oil but it belongs to the sea now, like they say, 'finders keepers'.

Bye, got to go, busy schedule and all.

Cathy Sillifant (13)
Budehaven Community School, Bude

Over The Rainbow

'Hey Mum, look at the rainbow, isn't it pretty?' I said as we were in the car on the way home. I wonder what is at the end of it?

The next day at school I asked my friends if they had seen the rainbow yesterday. All of them said yes and said how bright the colours were. So then I asked them what they thought was at the end of it.

Cassie said she thought there was lots of lovely gold at the end. Michael said he thought there was lots of golden honey at the end and Sheila even thought of pigs. I mean come on - pigs at the end of the rainbow?

When I got home would you believe it, there was another rainbow. This time, I was going to find out with my own eyes what was at the end of such a lovely rainbow. So I ran down the path, across the field through the woods and under the big, long gate. And then after all the running I finally came to the end, but there wasn't gold, honey or even pigs, there was just lovely green grass. So I walked back under the gate through the woods and across the field, then up the path and back home.

On Monday morning I told all my friends what was at the end of the rainbow and we were very upset, we just pretended to make ourselves happy. So now when people ask us what we think is at the end of the rainbow we tell them gold, honey and pigs!

Holly Kranat (12)
Budehaven Community School, Bude

Over The Rainbow

I used to dream about the other side of the rainbow, dream about what happiness there would be. In my dreams everybody was friends. There was no fighting or war but water, fountains, lakes; there were no diseases, illnesses or poverty in my dreams. But now my dreams have gone, my life around me is full of hatred and anger, rules, poverty, dying and diseases. It's too strong, too much to keep my lovely dreams the way they used to be. I'd do anything just to have those dreams again, maybe even just one, because it would make me feel like my life was worth living.

I'm Nadia, I come from a poor part of Africa. I live on the street with my brother Kasseri (4) and sister Tulsa (3). I look after both of them. They are the only things I've got left in my life, they give me the will to live. My mother and father died of AIDS a few years ago and now I have it. Every night I lie awake thinking about peace, trying so desperately hard to think about peace until I'm red in the face, just so I can have my dreams back again. But I can't think when there are noises around me. When I'm curled up with my brother and sister at night the thought of something happening to them scares me to death. What will they do when I'm gone? Will they go ... over the rainbow?

Esme Marshall (12)
Budehaven Community School, Bude

A Day In The Life Of A Vending Machine

I am all the time dropping out my supplies. As I get empty, I get unwell, very unwell. I can feel the scraping of the can, with a sudden drop on my bottom tray; it hurts so much, so very much. People bash me about and unplug me; sometimes I wake up and just remember switching off. It resets me. People are so cruel but I cannot blame them because they would not think about if a drinks machine has feelings or not. There is something that keeps me going though and that is the smile on people's faces when they drink something or eat something that I have given them, for a price obviously.

I get a tingling sensation in my wires when I am happy. I love younger kids and adults but not those horrible teenagers you get just out in the street who break or smash everything in sight. Without them, I would not be here now. I get so depressed when it is deserted.

Liam Smith (14)
Budehaven Community School, Bude

The Basement

I always wondered about the basement. What was down there? A monster, a giant or maybe just dust? It's always made me curious. Me and my sister Liz would always ask Mother if we were allowed but she said the same thing over and over again, 'Not till your father comes back,' she would say.

So I waited for ages just imagining Father coming through the door with his curly hair flapping in the wind. But one lucky evening the doorbell rang. I sprinted down the stairs hoping to see him and there he was, standing firmly in the doorway. He opened his arms and I jumped into them feeling his cold leather jacket. As he let go of his grip on me, I couldn't help but ask, 'Dad can we go into the basement?' With a large smile on his face, he reached into his pocket and pulled out a large rusted key which he dropped into my hands.

I ran as fast as I could to the large oak door which towered on top of me. As I slid the key into the door with a firm click, the door opened leading to a dusty path into the unknown.

As I stumbled down the creaky stairs, I felt a cold, solid floor below me. As I struck a match I could see three paths leading into more darkness. Thinking which one to take, my intelligent instincts told me to go into the left path. So I took the path not knowing what to find. As I crept quietly down the path, I heard a noise - not an ordinary one, a horrible dark sound. As my heart started to race faster and faster, suddenly out of the eerie darkness came a black shadow of a horned creature. I heard its footsteps getting closer and closer. I couldn't take it. I turned and ran. Panting wildly I burst into the kitchen and cried, 'Mum, where's Liz?'

She replied, 'Why, she is in the basement, dear.'

Sam Hunt (12)
Budehaven Community School, Bude

The Different Colours

It's funny isn't it what the sun and rain make, a rainbow. See when I was a kid ...

It was a chilly day when I heard a drip of rainfall onto my overcoat. It was yellow with a hat to match it. The next moment it was pouring down, water rushing down the rusty, metal gutters and then into the drains. I was watching the flow of the water as my nanny dragged me away. As I was pulled by my hand I looked up and saw these colours in the sky, bright and beautiful. With a blink of an eye it had faded, with a turn it vanished.

I was reading my book when my mother walked in saying, 'So what have you been doing today darling?'

'Not much,' I replied, as I knew she wasn't really interested. She would have probably said, 'That sounds interesting,' or something like that. But that second I thought, *no I'll tell her*. So I said, 'Actually I did do something today. I saw this weird colourful thing in the sky. It was there one moment and gone the next!'

'Oh that's called a rainbow darling. It's made from sun and water.'

I was so interested in the rainbow that I found out more and more, and many years later became a scientist, but I did not know that looking directly at the sun could damage your eyes until one day I couldn't see! The one thing I long for now is the colour to come back.

So next time you look at a rainbow don't let it vanish, stand and stare at its beauty because I've learnt from experience never let anything vanish.

Abigail Spry (12)
Budehaven Community School, Bude

The Fountains Of Mermaids

Have you ever wondered what's on the other side of the rainbow? Well I found out!

I was at school on a sunny day in my worst subject, maths, and I was so bored. Mr Linden was boring us about algebra so I decided to look out the window. This day couldn't get any worse.

Oh cheesy chops! It's just started to rain but it's sunny. Yes, there must be a rainbow! I turned to the boy next to me and said, 'What's on the other side of the rainbow?'

'You're mad!' he replied.

Suddenly I heard a soft voice saying, 'Follow the rainbow and you will find luck and joy!' I got so excited.

It was the end of the day so I started my quest at a well. I saw a girl there. 'What are you doing?' I asked her.

'I know it sounds stupid but ... following the rainbow,' she said.

'To find luck and joy? - So am I!' I said.

We looked up at the rainbow and started to follow it.

On the way I discovered that her name was Sahara but she didn't tell me where she came from, she just went quiet and smiled.

Sahara seemed to know the way - across rivers, through forests and then through a waterfall to a beautiful fountain. It was huge and there were mermaids swimming in it! Sahara jumped in and waved at me. I looked down, I was now a mermaid. So that's what's on the other side of the rainbow - the fountain of mermaids.

Lily Bolitho (12)
Budehaven Community School, Bude

Follow The Waves Home

Where am I?

Oh yeah, I remember!

It all started yesterday, Laura and I were out sailing our laser when it all happened.

I, Katie, 14, and my best mate Laura, 14, were out sailing off Plymouth Quay. A storm broke out and our boat went over. The sail ripped and the boat sank. I was so scared as I couldn't see Laura.

What happened next I can't remember but after that is so clear I will never forget it. I was breathing underwater. I had sunk with the ship.

It was really amazing because I had never heard of anyone going underwater and breathing.

When I reached the bottom I started to worry. I was asking myself questions. *What's happened to Laura? How am I going to get home?* I started walking one way then changed my mind and walked back the other way. I was so confused.

After walking for about an hour I looked up and decided I would follow the ripple of the waves home. The ripples were going east and that is where I came from.

I was walking for about two hours when I saw that the water was getting shallower. I was really excited, as I would be able to get home and tell my story. I was also upset and depressed because I'd lost Laura in the storm. I just didn't know how to explain.

Katharine Muller (11)
Budehaven Community School, Bude

Percy Saw It All

'I'm sorry, I promise it won't happen next time!' squealed Percy as he was caught red-handed stealing a pack of Haribo from the school canteen.

'There ain't gonna be no next time, Sonny!' roared Mrs Dung, our trampy textiles teacher who does the dinner lady job as well to get a bit of extra cash. She should spend the extra couple of quid on a new cardboard box. She's probably grown out of the one she slept in last night!

Anyway, my name is Cyril and I'm in Year 7. I go to Rudeheaven School and my best mate is Percy. Me and him always get away with stealing stuff, but I want to get caught more often because it's funny when Mrs Dung's voice gets angry. It is quality!

The other day Percy did get caught and he got taken to Mr Hellar's office. His office is right outside our RE room. Luckily enough, we had RE after break and we could hear him shouting at Percy. Our RE teacher, Miss Noble, had gone out of the room and left us, as usual.

Suddenly, a single gunshot silenced Rudeheaven.

We all stampeded into the corridor to catch Miss Noble shoving a smoking pistol into Miss Malter's pigeon hole. There, face down squirming in a pool of blood was Mr Hellars ...

George Swain (12)
Budehaven Community School, Bude

Follow The Waves

The crystal-blue waves crashed effortlessly against the hard wooden ship. The voyage had taken some days but the scruffy crew had managed to make it to the destination.

The captain of the ship was a young merry lad called Josh, who had lost both his father and mother at a young age, and now his small crew of eight men had taken him to the ship of his father.

He looked around eyeing everyone in turn. 'You two at the back take your diving equipment and be off, there isn't much time,' bellowed the stern captain.

They took their diving gear and were off into the water. They could see nothing at first, for it seemed like a black abyss ending in nothing but darkness, but soon they adjusted to the scenery and were well on their way; if it hadn't been for a very large storm emerging from the sky above.

They swam further and further until reaching the bottom and stared blankly at the old broken ship lying in front of them. They stood up and started to walk to the ship, but a fast current swept them off their feet and carried them in the opposite direction. Another wave came but this time it was aimed at the oxygen line. They fidgeted frantically but to no avail.

The captain had heard this through the microphone and had quickly turned his ship to shore. When he reached dry land he looked bleakly at the horizon and said, 'You will be safe with my father.'

Joshua Schouten de Jel (13)
Budehaven Community School, Bude

Life

Time. It's a weird thing but you know life is revolved around it. I don't bother using a watch or buying clocks, I just follow the waves.

Waves, how amazing are they? I mean they cover most of the Earth and how did they get here? Did they evaporate from the clouds? But where did the clouds come from? Life is so obscure, it's amazing people just get on with their lives and they don't look at the beautiful surroundings that fill the Earth.

Earth, it's a round ball but it's flat! It spins but how? I find it completely flabbergasting.

Another fascinating subject is people. No matter how hard you try you could do the most fantastic thing in the world and someone will have a problem with it!

Someone, everyone is different. They all have different characteristics, personalities and different looks but we're all the same. That's why I hate arguments; they're pointless really, they just cause people to get angry and upset. I'd love to be a boy, they just get on with life regardless. Whereas girls are a different matter! They snitch a lot of the time I don't see the point. Most of it's petty about what people look like and some of it's not even worth discussing as Forrest Gump says, 'Life is like a box of chocolates you never know which one you're going to get'!

Amy Porter (12)
Budehaven Community School, Bude

The Gasoline Rainbow

Sondorra strawberries. Produce of Mexico, read the label of the box I was mindlessly stacking in McAdam's Superstore. I never understood why they called it that, because in fact, there was nothing 'super' about it.

What would they label me if I were a box of fruit? *Sabina El Contorras. Produce of Mexico. Illegal goods.*

I was working the night shift, $2.25 an hour was my wage. It was much less than what the Americans got, but what could I do? I wasn't even supposed to be in the country and my employers knew. The food I stacked had more rights than me. Still, it was twice as much as I had been earning picking strawberries in the sweltering fruit fields back home.

I caught a ride in Mr Singh's car. I much prefer donkeys. They're more reliable and you can have conversations with them. I know all they can do is hee-haw back, but I like to believe that they understand. I told Mr Singh, but he just laughed at me.

The car sped away, leaving behind a spurious rainbow of gasoline. The last time I'd caught sight of a rainbow, Mama and I were trying to cross the border into California. She told me the rainbow was leading me to a better life. But now I was in America, all I wanted to do was go home to real rainbows. Instead, I was left alone to stare at my reflection in the phoney gasoline rainbow beneath me.

Sophie Thomsett (14)
Budehaven Community School, Bude

Just One Person, Just Nine Words

As I am travelling down the corridor, I watch people, see the disgust etched into their faces, cruelty and malice changing their expressions.

They think I can't hear or see them. Maybe I can't sometimes, but I can right now. They make my heart weep, make me weep. Not from pain, but pity. Pity for them.

I am dismissed in an instant, maybe one day, I will be able to enter a room without fear wrapping itself around me, making a barricade which cannot be broken.

I have to earn the right to live, to exist. I earned the right to be born, but not to lead a normal life.

People see my problem first. They don't see me, they don't see I am a kind, friendly human. Some people are frightened of me, petrified I could contaminate them, infect them, thus passing 'it' on.

I see it in their eyes, their minds clicking furiously, sickly fascinated, seeing the heap of metal I am sitting in.

So ... I am sitting in a wheelchair, my legs burnt beyond recognition. Only one person has seen beyond the burnt flesh and metal. She passed me in the corridor, just once. Looked at me and smiled. All she had to say, all that had to be said were in those nine words. In that instant, I knew I could succeed. All that changed my life forever, were nine single words.

'I believe in you. I believe you can walk.'

Katie Mellett (15)
Budehaven Community School, Bude

The Shadow

The sea was a calm length of bejewelled blue, clear as a sunlit crystal, glimmering as the turquoise waves went dancing up the rise of smooth, white sand, lapping the rocks like a huge, elegant cat, the pure snowy white foam embedded the rocks.

A shadow underwater. A fishtail sculpted out of shimmering blue, purple and seaweed-green penetrated the cobalt surface, breaking the peaceful silence.

A strong, slim body rose out of the water, beads of water shone like diamonds and rubies, amethysts and opals.

The fireball of a sun gasped in astonishment at the awesome sight, the mighty heavens looked on in wonder. The mermaid dived down to the seabed, swimming gracefully between the dazzling greens of the plants growing up from the brilliant sand, shiny shells shone brightly in the sunlight filled ocean.

And she was gone.

Beth Whitlock (12)
Budehaven Community School, Bude

Follow The Waves

As the sun rose in the summer sky the town was a hive of activity. It was the day we had all been waiting for. The day of the voyage that was going to change history forever, or that's what they hoped.

I for one could not see how a group of enthusiastic fishermen could really discover unknown land. We may have been led by a well educated navigator but this was not the point. I was one of them, I knew what I was capable of doing. It had already brought us fame and who knows it could bring us riches too.

Wherever I went I was reminded of what I had let myself in for. As I entered the pub I was greeted by many cheers. What I did not get was we had not done anything yet.

The ship looked so impressive anchored in the small port. It was to be my home for the best part of my youth and its intricate figurehead was very grand.

The noisy crowd on the shoreline got bigger. It seemed the whole town had gathered to wave us off. As I hoisted the anchor a tear rolled down my cheek. This was it. The final farewell to life as I knew it. We waved until they were nothing but black dots on the horizon then the land slipped away and we were alone with the ocean.

Emily King (12)
Budehaven Community School, Bude

The Black Hat

October 3rd 1930, 7.15pm

It all started when I got the call. 'Hello ... there's been a murder ... come quickly ... 94 Chapel Terrace.'

It wasn't often I received a call like this. I grabbed my hat and walked out of the door onto the mist shrouded streets of New York. I got into my car and started the engine.

94 Chapel Terrace appeared to be a normal block of flats, but my gut told me it was more. I walked through the door. The foyer was empty besides one person. 'Are you the investigator?' he said.

'Nick Smith at your service,' I replied.

'Come with me.' The man, who I found out was the manager, led me to room 106 and showed me inside. On the floor there lay a limp body. On the man's chest there was a black hat. This was the calling card of Johnathan Aberdechi, the biggest player in the Big Apple's underworld. This was serious.

This man must have either been very brave or very stupid to get mixed up with someone like Aberdechi. This was how most people who met him ended up. Investigating this murder would make me a player in a very dangerous game, a very dangerous game indeed.

James Savage (12)
Budehaven Community School, Bude

A Day In The Life Of A Soldier

I wake up at four in the morning. I know that I've got a big day ahead of me. I'm going into battle today - Iraq. I gently put on my uniform making sure there are no creases.

Today I'm going to be flying over the country, landing in air base in Baghdad. On board will be myself, Corporal Sanders and Corporal Johns: we are going to be leading the attack. Our mission is to rescue two hostages who are being held by Iraqi terrorists. They are armed so we must be careful but quick.

As we fly over the land, I can see evidence of fighting war. There are fires all around from burning buildings. Bodies lying on the ground. I begin to shake a little but I've done this before so I quickly get back to my normal self.

The helicopter touched down softly into the centre of the city. A tank filled with British troops has come to join us. They will be our back-up later.

We drive off all together, looking for the building where the hostages are being held. The sergeant has found a tracking device. This is our chance, our chance to get them.

At last we have found the building. We need to find out the final team and move in. We break down the door with a metal bar.

With our shields held high, we raid the building. When we find the hostages, they are tied up, but there is no sign of the terrorists. They must have fled when they heard our tanks. We may not be as lucky next time ...

Robert Bluett (12)
Budehaven Community School, Bude

A Day In The Life Of A Pebble

A pebble lies on a grey rocky beach. In the morning a fisherman stomps over it with his heavy black boots. Then just after noon the tide comes in and washes it out to the deep blue sea. It stumbles, seeing many wonderful and colourful fish. But one time it sees a great, dark, basking shark. It's the biggest thing it's ever seen.

The pebble sees many things. There are lots of creatures on the seabed. This time it goes through a shipwreck. It sees a rotting piano and a grand fireplace. It comes out the other side to see more wonderful things. The pebble starts to bob along the seabed. It sees many magnificent types of seaweed. It then stops on the sand. It looks around and spots gleaming shoals of sardines. It then starts to use other senses. It can hear dolphins speaking in the distance. Also it can feel the salt scraping on its smooth body. Then the sea starts to move again. The pebble is lifted from the sand again. Suddenly the tide goes out very fast.

It ends up on the best beach ever. It sees the powdery yellow sand. A great hotel gleaming on the cliff. It can smell the wonderful sea air around it. It then waits on the soft sand for its next adventure.

Adam Collins (12)
Budehaven Community School, Bude

What's Over The Rainbow?

'Hurry up Jenny,' shouted Katie running towards the dance hall. Then when it started to rain, 'Look there's a bus shelter,' called Katie from behind. We ran over to the bus shelter. We sat there for 10 minutes eating our ham sandwiches we were saving for our dance club. 'I think the rain is stopping and look, there is a rainbow,' Katie cried.

'I wonder what's over the rainbow?' I said and at that a light shone down on me. It was lifting me into the sky.

I woke up feeling very tired. I looked around, my eyes still blurred. All I saw were flowers. I was in a garden. I stood up, shook off the dirt and started making my way up the garden. There was a variety of flowers - bluebells, roses and poppies. There was a swing. It was very old and battered. I saw a rusty iron door. I walked over to the door and gave it a hard push. It was hard to open but I did it. I walked through a lot of the garden till I came to a big house. It was a strange place. I thought, *never go home.* Suddenly I saw what I thought was a ghost. It was.

'Hello,' I called.

He spoke. He said, 'This is what's over the rainbow.'

The same light came back.

I was back at the bus shelter like nothing had happened. Katie was standing over me. 'Are you all right?' asked Katie.

'Yes,' I said.

I stood up. Katie and I walked down the quiet street all the way home.

Hannah Crook (12)
Budehaven Community School, Bude

A Day In The Life Of A Pound Coin

I woke up to the sweet smell of syrup and waffles. I was lying on the kitchen table waiting for Derrick to pick me up for his school dinner. He picked me up and shoved me in his pocket. He ran out of the door and got on the school bus. He was just about to sneeze so he reached into his pocket and pulled out a tissue. Without realising I fell on the school bus floor rolling around. As we went up the hill I slowly rolled down to a very big pair of shoes. A very large girl picked me up and held me all the way to the bus stop as if she didn't want me to leave. She ran out of the bus to the nearest sweet shop and bought a tub of marshmallows.

Now I was in a smelly old till. The next customer came in and bought a loaf of bread and some milk. So I happened to become someone's change. I felt the lady's phone go off. When she answered it, it was Derrick telling his mum that he had lost his dinner money, so she ran straight to the car and drove to school. She ran straight to the reception where she met Derrick and gave him his lunch money back.

Jessica Rash (14)
Budehaven Community School, Bude

Over The Rainbow

This is a story about Jess who had always been curious about just one thing, what was at the other end of the rainbow?

It was a rather nice sunny day as Jess was getting out of bed. When she looked out the window she noticed a faded rainbow in the distance.

Today Jess' parents were going out for the day, so as she was eating her breakfast she planned what she was going to do for the day. What a surprise she had planned to leave early and complete her dream. She was going to follow the rainbow.

She left home early, took her binoculars, a compass, some crisps and a drink. She headed off north looking at the rainbow at all times making sure not to lose sight of it. After an hour of walking she came to some sort of magical land where there were rabbits with three ears and more unusual animals. At this time Jess was really excited about finding the end and getting home to tell her parents.

Wow, it was the end of the rainbow and what people had told Jess was true, there was a pot of gold at the end.

Jess started to make her way home. It only took her three hours and her parents were home. When she told them where she had been they didn't believe her, but where had the pot of gold gone? She had lost it on the way home. Now no one would believe her. What should she do?

Harriet Hunter (12)
Budehaven Community School, Bude

A Day In The Life Of A Fairy

I woke up and ran downstairs for breakfast. When I went into the kitchen there seemed to be a strange atmosphere between my mum and dad so I walked away. As I walked through the hallway I could hear Dad talking. 'We are going to send her away. It's only a month.'

'No, you can't send Twinkle Toes to the cattery. I won't see her again.' Mum started to cry.

'Thumberlina we aren't talking about your stupid cat we are talking about you.'

I was so angry that I ran upstairs and packed my bags and stood in front of the car. When we got there my mum tried to give me a kiss and I pushed her away and walked off.

I've now been here for months and it's my first potions and wishing spell lesson. My first wish was that my mum and dad wouldn't come to pick me up. I didn't think it would come true so I carried on making the potion.

My mum and dad are coming to see me tomorrow and for some reason I'm quite excited. I was woken up in the middle of the night by the head of the fairies. She brought me downstairs and said, 'Your mum and dad have been involved in a car crash and have died.'

I knew it was my fault so I ran into the potions room and drank one of them.

So here I am telling my story in Heaven.

Sarah Bartlett (12)
Budehaven Community School, Bude

A Day In The Life Of A Slave

I woke up this morning to find myself face to face with the floor. I don't know how I got there seeing as my hands were tied to a wooden support pole. My head was hurting so I thought that there must have been a big storm that night. That doesn't explain how my hands became untied though. Okay, maybe it wasn't a storm but whatever it was, it hurt my head. Anyway I sat up and moved to the pole I'd been tied to. (Better not let the sailors see I'm free, it upsets them a bit.)

I'd been leaning against the pole for about five minutes when down came breakfast. Slops and water. Yum. The food on this ship is about as nice to eat as chewing a wasp.

I won't bore you with the whole day so I'll leave out the boring bits. Some time after *breakfast*, we were allowed up on deck. It was so good to feel the sun's rays beating down on me and to see the spray jumping up in front of the ship like the dust from the back of a herd of wildebeest.

Now it's the end of the day and I still can't believe the moon we see from this ship is the same one we saw from the plains of Africa. I wonder sometimes if I'll ever see the moon from Africa again.

Duncan Smith (12)
Camborne Science & Community College, Camborne

A Day In The Life Of A Slave

I woke up this morning to find myself in the same miserable nightmare, except this time I won't wake up.

I'm fed up of this, fed up of sleeping in my own filth, fed up of having no one to talk to. I could just about bear it when the old woman was here to tell me her Anansi stories, but the big white men moved her, so now it's just me and my confused thoughts.

I hate it here, I'm treated like a number, like I'm not human. Mama said I'm being taken somewhere I can be free; somewhere I can live without fear. Maybe that's why it's so horrible, so I will suffer and then be taken to some sort of paradise. Also with the big white men there is a boy the same age as me. When he comes he just stares and when he stares he looks so pitiful, it makes me wonder if he is a new type of white man. He seems loving and true, but I can't be sure because when he speaks I can't understand him, he speaks a funny language.

Now the only thing that keeps me sane is Anansi. His quick-witted, sharp-minded tales never cease to amaze me, even if I make them up myself. But for now I have to sit here in all this misery, death and despair, all alone with only my free mind to talk to.

Sarah Guerandel (12)
Camborne Science & Community College, Camborne

A Day In The Life Of An African Slave

I woke up this morning drenched in the salty water of the sea. The hard wooden floorboards were creaking beneath my feet. My breakfast arrived (or what's meant to be my breakfast). I began to eat, I was absolutely starving, I hadn't had any food for two days. But it didn't really taste of anything at all, it was rice, stale bread and a glass of water.

It's so boring on this ship the only part of me that feels free is my imagination. I am missing my mum and thinking of how nice it would be back home compared to this miserable, dark and gloomy boat.

The captain has made a new rule on the boat, every slave must have at least 10 minutes every day of fresh air on deck. I try and take in as much as I can and savour the moment. I don't know how much longer I can survive. I will survive, I'm not going to give up now, I will not die.

Jacob Kemp (12)
Camborne Science & Community College, Camborne

A Day In The Life Of An African Slave

I am here, being sold like an antique. What has become of me? I was happy at home with Ma. I miss the smell of the sweet flowers and the hum of the bees. The only noise I have to comfort me is the hustle of people and the knock of the hammer.

I miss the soft grass tickling my cheek as I lay in the warm midday sun. I miss the voice of my family and tribe and the smell of my mother's cooking. I miss being me, I will be reunited one day, somehow.

I'm next to be sold. There's a girl in front of me being sold now, she looks terrified. Maybe I look like her, terrified eyes that will soon rain, an upside down smile never to be turned, a body so thin it will break in a blink.

I have to stand in front of peering eyes glaring at me. A man's saying things. What's happening, why is this man grabbing at me? Why is he leading me away? Where am I going? *Get off me!* I'm outside, the air smells good, I'm on a road, a crossroad.

Poppy Mitchell (12)
Camborne Science & Community College, Camborne

A Day In The Life Of A Slave

After the auction the girl is taken off to a massive new house. Her courage is being put to the test, but she thinks of clever new Anansi stories to help her. Her master and mistress are white folk and she does not understand the strange language they speak. They are not as horrible as the men on the boat.

The girl isn't scared anymore, she has been given a new name, Makosi and a nice little place of her own for when she is not working.

The Anansi stories help her (she says), they make her feel stronger and cheer her up when she's sad or upset. They remind her of the woman on the boat and her much missed home in Africa, where she hopes her mother and father and family are safe and well.

Sometimes she wants to go back home to Africa. She knows she cannot go at the present time but hopes that when she is older she can go back to the home she once lived happily in.

Merryn Williams (12)
Camborne Science & Community College, Camborne

A Day In The Life Of An African Slave

1756 - I have been captured and put on a dirty ship. I was thrown down a set of stairs and tied back to back to a woman on a pole. There are lots of other people down here who have already caught the disease which is going around the ship. I'm really scared that I'm going to catch the disease and die. I don't want to die, I'm only 8 years old, I'm too young to die.

I miss my mum and my dad and my baby sister Khadija! At the moment I am homesick. Every night I cry myself to sleep because I'm scared and missing my family.

I vaguely remember my family. I have no picture of them to hold on to every minute of every day. The only way I remember them is in my mind.

I wonder what they're doing now. If I could contact them, somehow, I would say to them not to worry about me, I'm safe. To say to them that I love them and maybe one day we'll be reunited in Heaven.

Nicole Curnow (12)
Camborne Science & Community College, Camborne

A Day In The Life Of An African Slave

My name is Zlata and I am an African slave. I work for a wealthy woman, helping her dress and wash. I also help her into town. She is cruel and scolds me often, saying that I am stupid and ignorant. He says that, but she's the one who never lifts a finger. The town is a smelly place; it smells of rotten fish and oil. I would give anything to go back to Africa. It smells clean and fresh.

I have a room the size of a cupboard and I own nothing apart from a few clothes, a towel and a toothbrush. From the few bits of money I earn I have bought a hairbrush, but I mostly spend it on a few treats like cakes! I haven't any friends, besides I would not be allowed to see them. There is a small black cat that comes to see me. I give him some scraps and a stroke. My mistress hates any animals, especially cats.

Her husband just looks at me like dirt. They laugh at my expense, saying how dirty and ugly I am. I don't know where my mother is or even if she is alive. Oh I think I shall die soon of misery and grief.

Joanne Rolling (12)
Camborne Science & Community College, Camborne

Nothing's Changed

Tatamkulu walked alongside the lonely road. He dragged his feet one after another. Tall purple flowers reached high among the seeded grasses. With every step he took he could feel the stony ground digging into his heels. He was surrounded by weeds and debris of old buildings that had been razed to the ground. It was a desolate area; the abandoned sea.

It seemed everywhere he looked his home town had been boarded off, segregated to a fragment of places. How could a loving, mixed community of people be turned against each other by so-called 'authority'? It made Tatamkulu angry, this was his home. But he was forced to face the reality put into order by the monster that was Apartheid.

He spotted a new, up-market inn. Whites only. The guard at the gatepost glared at him. His beady eyes watching Tatamkulu's every step, hungry for a wrong move. The glass pane felt cool against his nose, the air around him was unforgivingly dry. He spotted a glass of sparkling ice and a brilliant red rose perched on top of the linen-draped table.

'Oi! Back up rat.'

Tatamkulu left with a bitter taste in his mouth. If only he had the chance to smash through the barrier. How could something be so evil as to allow his whole culture to turn his back on him? To leave him alone to pick up the pieces and hope that just one day things might be different. Tatamkulu walked away. Nothing's changed.

Heidi Cottam (14)
Camborne Science & Community College, Camborne

24 Hours Of A Garbage Man

I woke up early that morning, much like the mornings before that. I'd had little to eat since the previous morning. I get grief every time I go to collect the rubbish from houses, I think it is because of the stench the lorry leaves behind every pick-up we make.

The other day I got my wages deducted as I quite often get to work late. It has been a long time since I have had a cooked meal, I usually have the microwave meals. When I get to work I get changed into my green trousers, black work boots, my green T-shirt with fluorescent vest and most importantly my gloves. When I'm changed I go down to the dustbin lorry and check the map so I know where I'm going. And then we're off!

Usually before we get to the destination we stop at McDonald's for a quick bite to eat. After that we carry on with the job. We do about five or six houses before the first insult gets chucked at me, they always moan about the smell of the lorry but we're only doing our job. Finally, when the day is over I go home with a small, yet well deserved pay check.

Nathan Barnard (14)
Camborne Science & Community College, Camborne

A Day In The Life Of A Vietnamese Village Man

The destruction had been continuous throughout the night. As it was every night, as it had been for the last two years.

Life in this beautiful village had been destroyed by the invasive conquest of the western man. I had raised a family and lived in the most beautiful peaceful place for over 70 years. Now, as I sat poised in my oak-carved bed, looking upon a forest of unimaginable beauty, I saw what it was and then I realised that all the time I was in my bed whiling away the day in a remote community that based its structure on respect and teamwork, I was missing the bigger picture.

There was an abundance of suffering and death. I may have been old and well ... a bit worse for wear, but I could still help. Why was I sitting in this hospital whilst the world wept at my door?

I grabbed my coat and left the ward.

Along the endless track that led up to the hospital, I saw what I never had imagined possible. A man, crawling along the dust track. His left leg, absent. A gushing wound had made him weak. I ran to him. Threw him upon my shoulder and carried him to my bed.

The afternoon drew to an end and the man was left to rest. All that could be done, had been. But as the sun set and as with many a brave man life was not granted to this young warrior.

Seth Holt
Camborne Science & Community College, Camborne

Dustcart Vs Mercedes

I had been up since 4am in the dampness of the morning lifting bins full of other people's garbage and loading onto the truck and watching the rubbish get crushed. My life feels so rubbish and boring, moving around other people's junk. I wish I had a nice car instead of moving around in a smelly old truck. Working in the stench of the rubbish I can't help that my clothes smell. I guess I've just got used to it.

I don't get home till late and I don't go to sleep for long and then I have to get up in the morning again early. One day whilst moving the rubbish around early in the morning I saw a nice Mercedes and its lights flash on my orange top. I got out of my truck and stared down at the flash car and the man and the woman sitting in it with nice clothes and blonde hair wearing expensive sunglasses and they both looked happy. Then I looked at the bin men and they looked the complete opposite. The posh people didn't even turn their heads to look at us, as if we were nothing, like rats. If I am honest I would do anything to be like them and have a car like that and dress like that and to not smell of the disgusting stench of rubbish and sweat. Oh how I really wish I had a car like that!

Adam Barry (13)
Camborne Science & Community College, Camborne

24 Hours In The Life Of A Slave

Dear Diary,

Once again I woke up to the ringing of the bell. The sign of another long, exhausting day ahead of me. I couldn't bring myself to drag myself off the cold, wooden floorboards of the ship, so as usual, about ten minutes later I had the master come round with his cane. Let's just say I had to struggle to keep myself from falling to the ground. My head's been spinning around all day. The heat was so intense today I had to take every opportunity I could to keep out of the scorching sun.

My life is completely torn. I was all right with my last master, he was nice to me and never hit me with anything as long as I did all of his work for him, he'd be kind. Now I'm trapped here just because he found someone better to work for him. I don't understand. Well, he can go to Hell then, seeing as I'm already in Hell.

There's this game we all made up, it's called 'Limbo', it's quite fun but only if we have time. It gives me peace of mind, makes me reflect on my life. Not that it's all that great. I mean look at me, I'm stuck here lying across from wounded friends. I've no family and I'm getting beaten every day. But my heart goes out to this poor young boy who was hung for stealing some rice. God bless him.

Natalie Brookes
Camborne Science & Community College, Camborne

A Day In The Life Of A Slave

Dear Diary,

My first day on the slave ship. People were screaming, shouting and crying for their families. It was torture. We went to sleep the first night. It didn't seem as bad as we thought it would, but the morning, now that was a whole different thing.

We had to wake up at 4.30am. I didn't want to, but the creatures were walking around with sticks. We each got hit at the start of the day as a warning and a scare. They said, 'This is a warning, if you misbehave at all, or we think you do, then you'll get it ten times as hard or just until you bleed.'

We got up and if we needed the toilet we had to go in one of the corners. I was given a scrub and a bucket of cold, dirty water. One of them shouted at me, 'Scrub you dirty animal! Clean the floors. You'll have to get used to this!'

A tear ran down my cheek. I wiped it away thinking of my family back in Africa, too weak to travel or be a slave. I scrubbed, scrubbed harder and was made to scrub even longer. My knees were cut, I wasn't allowed to stop. When I stopped it was 3pm.

I was given another job. I had to collect one of the dead babies and throw it overboard. Afterwards, they grabbed me and beat me to a pulp for fun. Slaves will get revenge.

Sadie Saunders
Camborne Science & Community College, Camborne

A Day In The Life Of A Slave

I wake up at 5am to a ship covered in dirt and urine. We have some breakfast which is food that's been chewed by rats. We start to sail about 6am to an unknown place that no one knows. The smell is horrific and it's getting worse by the second.

It's 12am and we are still sailing and people are starving and are desperate for food. The weather is getting worse and worse, the rain is lashing down. People's spirits are going down so we all limbo to try and lift our spirits.

It's 3pm and the rain has died down. The rain has been dripping into the cabin all day and now there isn't a dry space on the ship. Our clothes are wet and the smell is dreadful. People are now suffering as they are starving.

It's 6pm and we get the first piece of food since 5am this morning. We finish eating and we try and start to get rid of the water on the ship. After we've done that it gets dark and it's time to go down to the cabin for the night, but first we have one last limbo to keep spirits rising as the white man can never take this away from us. It's been a long day.

Gavin Tregenza
Camborne Science & Community College, Camborne

24 Hours In The Life Of A Slave

Early one morning I awoke to the stench of urine lingering in the air. It was a bumpy ride on the ship full of slaves. Babies crying maybe even dying, others dying of diseases. I was at the bottom of the ship in a small box, we were all so skinny so we could all fit in. But we couldn't go to the toilet we had to go there, in our clothes. I couldn't believe the way they were treating us. They beat us with a whip, shouted at us, they sometimes even beat us till people were dead.

The moaning of screaming of people getting beaten is going to haunt me for the rest of my life. Every night I have a nightmare about the pain we went through. How could they do this to us? We're human beings too. I can't explain what it was like, the way we sat in our own urine and waste was disgusting, but we could do nothing about it. There was a man I knew, they beat him, tied him up so he couldn't move and beat him black and blue for no reason. They thought it would be fun, it's disgusting, horrible, the way those people could treat other human beings like this.

I heard there was a new game that someone made up they call it the limbo I haven't had a go yet. I don't like it here I hope it all ends soon.

Steven James (14)
Camborne Science & Community College, Camborne

24 Hours In The Life Of A Slave

Early one morning I awoke to the stench of urine lingering in the air. It was a bumpy ride on this ship full of slaves. Babies crying maybe even dying, other's dying of diseases. I was at the bottom of the ship in a small box, we were all so skinny so we could all fit in. But we couldn't go to the toilet we had to go there in our clothes. I couldn't believe the way they were treating us. They beat us with a whip, shouted at us, they sometimes even beat us till people were dead.

The moaning of screaming of people getting beaten is going to haunt me for the rest of my life. Every night I have a nightmare about the pain we went through. How could they do this to us? We're human beings too. I can't explain what it was like, the way we sat in our own urine and waste was disgusting, but we could do nothing about it. There was a man I knew, they beat him, tied him up so he couldn't move and beat him black and blue for no reason. They thought it would be fun, it's disgusting, horrible, the way those people could treat other human beings like this.

I heard there was a new game that someone made up they call it the limbo I haven't had a go yet. I don't like it here I hope it all ends soon.

Gareth Harris (14)
Camborne Science & Community College, Camborne

Nightmare At Check-In

It was Monday afternoon 12.30 to be exact and I'd just been picked for the school's field trip to France.

I'd never been on a field trip before, as soon as the bell rang at 3.15 I couldn't get out there any quicker even if I was playing football!

When I got home I told my mum, it was the worst thing I have ever done.

'Make sure you've got your pants. Do you want your lucky underwear with the frogs on them?'

'Mum I'm fifteen I don't wear them anymore!' I packed my gear like shirts, hats, shades and my toiletries read to leave on Friday.

Friday came so quickly, 'Mum hurry up we're going to be late!' We got to the checkout point.

'Have you got your passport?' The check-in lady enquired.

'Noo! I've forgotten my passport.' I rang my mum. 'Mum I've forgotten my passport. Can you go and get it for me? Thanks, love ya.' Mum was just around the corner so she got there quickly.

'I said have you got everything, but because you were in such a rush you forgot it.'

'Have you got your passport?' the check-in lady said. I gave her it, then she laughed at the picture.

My heart started to sink, I could already tell what this field trip was going to be like.

Jahmal Johnson
Coxlease School, Lyndhurst

Horror Teacher

Once upon a time on a cold winter's morning I had a new teacher.

A bat flew through the open window and with a puff of smoke a woman appeared next to the white board.

She said her name was *Mrs Gammon!* I was scared because of the puff of smoke and this made me wonder if she was a vampire. I began to feel anxious because of her *big teeth!* These showed when she sneered.

Mrs Gammon was around my neck. She said I would be nice to eat. I was doing my work when she shut the window and the door and it was dark like Hell! She said, 'We are not allowed to have any light in the room!'

I was eating my lunch and she came in with a chicken sandwich and a chicken leg. She was eating it like a vampire, devouring it. This made me worried I was going to be next for her lunch.

I was playing football when I saw Mrs Gammon running after a kid. Then I ran to help the kid out but she ran away.

She went home to her hovel which was located in wasteland near a place which some people said was haunted.

I was going out with my mate and I saw a vampire flying through the air and it freaked me out, then she came down to say, 'I am going to kill you little boy.'

Then my mates tried to kill the vampire by running into the light but she saw it and she covered herself.

She disappeared into thin air.

We went to my house and said to my mum, 'Don't go out of the house.'

She said, 'Why?'

'There's a vampire on the loose.'

My mate and I went to my bedroom to think of a plan to kill the vampire.

'The only way to kill the vampire is to push a metal stake through the heart!'

'It's going to be Mrs Gammon's birthday in eight weeks' time. That's when she dies!' I replied.

We went to the graveyard and we saw a bat flying, it seemed to be following us!

My mates and I hid near the graveyard to see if we could see the vampire.

We were waiting for the day to come to kill the vampire.

Eight weeks later Mrs Gammon's birthday arrived and we brought a present, it was a metal stake! When Mrs Gammon opened the present she had a surprised and worried look on her face.

Then we took the stake and stabbed through her heart, and then she said, 'Why?'

'Because you are a vampire!' we replied.

She turned to dust and was never seen again.

The school was happy. They had a party!

Eliott Beach
Coxlease School, Lyndhurst

The Cat

I'm *sooo* hungry. I'm fed up now, I'm waking Mum up. Great she's up now. That was easy, all I had to do was sit on her head!

That breakfast was great. I had rabbit casserole. Let's see, oh yeah time to wait outside for that midget mutt, he's smaller than me. I can see him coming down the road; yes he's seen me, and he's started to panic, he's just in front of me. I leap out and chase him up he road, he sure can run fast!

Yes! Everyone's leaving for school or work. That means I can go and sleep in Mum's sink, for some reason she doesn't let me when she's using it. Oh thank God there's no water in there this time, I hate it when that happens. I'm only going to take a little power nap. Mmm, OK this is nice but I think I'm going to try the washing basket. Well this is nice but I can think of something better, oh yeah the window sill. This is great but I'm going back to the sink. This is much better.

Nina pulls me out of the sink and carried me upstairs. Then she lays me on her bed. That's typical, I was just getting comfortable in the sink, but this, mmm, is nice.

'Night Cocoa,' Nina says to me, and she turns out the light. I just purr and Nina scratches my ears. I can feel my eyes get heavy. I'm sooo tired.

Shawnee Middleton-Darby (13)
Downlands Community School, Hassocks

Snake Skin

The ground pounded, it put its head back and sniffed, Man was near. This snake could tell, ever since a baby was killed, Man had been hunting him; it had been like that for over five months now, when he heard the sound he hid, the sound of feet, the smell of fire, the sight of the skin. As the snake thought to himself, *thank God I am able to lose my skin, Man is stuck with his*.

A sudden noise interrupted the snake, it was not the usual sound of feet but a low thumping and a soft ticking, suddenly through the trees a half elephant, half lion, and half bird. Even though this creature was rare the snake knew of this monster a beast that the Devil himself made, personally made, he put his own skin on it, his own blood running in its veins, his own brain telling it what to do.

Connor Oakley (13)
Five Islands School, Isles of Scilly

A Day In The Life Of A Sniper

He stared at the pools of light flooding through the semicircular glass Victorian panelled windows that characterised the platform in Paddington. He had given up looking at the four-sided hanging clock; it only made him anxious. He realised it was probably a bad idea to stand on Paddington's main platform with the largest bunch of red flowers he could find. Half the population of England now thought he was a weirdo, a prostitute or a loser.

Today was a bad day for him: four botched jobs and one ripped Stetson. He lay down on a rusty girder supporting the roof. He unclipped his case, took off his brown Stetson and laid it down beside him. He fixed the sight to his gun, cupped it to his eye, took a deep breath, clasped the trigger and adjusted his position. He moved the barrel to get the man in the crosshairs. To him the man was just that: a man, or not even that. He liked to think of him as £250,000. He held his breath and pulled the trigger. That was it.

On reflection, today had been pretty bad; he had wasted £15 on a ridiculous bunch of flowers, £150 on a pointless three-piece suit and £10 on an arrogant taxi driver from North London. He felt a soft pain in his neck. It was kind of relieving: his body felt so light and so redeemed. He fell to the floor and everything went black; he caught a glimpse of a tall man replacing a Stetson and walking off into the distance. Everything went white; he remembered his gas bill.

Alexander Hygate (13)
Five Islands School, Isles of Scilly

The Jattajay

On a tempestuous evening, in the middle of Alaska, an insidious, blood-drenching monster appeared, looking for the meat of a human. His name was Jattarjay. His fingers were as sharp as hawks' talons, eyes glaring red like the fiery life in Hell.

Even if you think he was evil he could definitely not be, seeing how he was a vegetarian. He was simply scouting out for meat for his Mother, but he still didn't find the flesh and bones of anyone; instead he mixed up leaves, mud and branches. That could explain why his mother was so ill.

'Mother I'm home. I got you the flesh of a little girl, sweet but sour, it's delicious,' said the Jattajay.

'Dear, I'm glad you're not like your father, he wouldn't wish to catch humans for me, seeing how he is a ...' she sobbed and spoke again in a hushed voice. 'Well he's a *vegetarian,* brought shame on this family. He was a herbivore.' His mother slowly fell back to sleep again.

'Mother I'm a ... a *vegetarian* too,' whimpered the Jattajay quietly, but his mother was fast asleep by this time.

The Jattajay sat silently outside his worn out leaf-ridden cave. *Oh dear, how will Mother ever know, and if I, if I tell her she will never forgive me, never look at me again, I'll be an outcast, I'll be my father!* thought the Jattajay nervously.

The Jattajay had no idea what he was going to do: admit he was a vegetarian and become an outcast like his scum of a father, or keep feeding his mother food and killing her, or start to eat humans, meat and his friends. He just couldn't do it.

He sat there day and night deciding until it came to that day ...

Keren Ware (12)
Five Islands School, Isles of Scilly

The Night Of The Goblin

It's the night of the goblin; one hundred years have passed, for the night of the goblin is tonight. You can feel the fear of everyone that knows it. You are in your house and you hear a little creak, you turn around and the door is open, you are oblivious to how it happened. You then realise that the goblin is in your house. It eats your food, it drinks your water, but you will not attempt to stop it because you are cold with fear.

You have heard the legends and they make you insecure, yet it may be the wind. That is what you should keep thinking, yet the worst version of the legend is always on your mind. You have been told that it eats young children. You can hear it coming up the stairs; they are creaking. Each creak is like a bone breaking in your body that stands up to fear. You can now smell it and it makes you want to be sick. You do not know whether it is fear or the smell that makes you feel sick. You can taste the coldness of the goblin and how it does not care for human life. You can smell the fearful aroma of the goblin's dark brain. You can see the goblin's mouldy teeth and human flesh around its mouth. Yet you are not scared for you know you are going to die.

James Hicks (12)
Five Islands School, Isles of Scilly

The Setting For My Dream

There was a frozen river called Fred. Each side of Fred there were forests. 10 foot tall ukulele playing hamsters square danced around the ice. The animals, birds and the weather all resembled the big toe of Harry's pet pelican. (Harry is my townie brudah.)

And looking through the rotten dust you could see 101 different types of fungi, each more green than the last (except for number #39 which was pink!) The place was swarming with rusty railings and wasps, (that couldn't play the steel drums for their lives).

On the other side of the river, the bearded lady sat and rapped 24/7 whilst robotic cannonballs rolled around her stool, (which was made of pine). Also, Stacey's mom (who's got it going on) rolled around the stool like some crazy conspiracy.

Sam Ellis (13)
Five Islands School, Isles of Scilly

A Day In The Life Of My Mum!

I can still remember that day, the day I swapped lives with my mum.

I woke up the sweat dripping off my face! I got up and thought it was just a normal day. But I was wrong. As I stood up and looked in the mirror I let out a huge scream! I looked up and down the mirror in amazement, I couldn't believe it. It wasn't me I was ... my mum!

I had to act quickly, I realised soon that if I was my mum then she would be me! I knew that I had to take control and get my mum to school on time!

Abbigail Hutchins (13)
Five Islands School, Isles of Scilly

A Day In The Life Of Tony Blair

Dear Diary,

Today is the election and I have visited over half of England to persuade all those unimportant people to vote for my campaign. I am one of the most popular people in England.

Getting back to me now, as I am the best, they are bound to vote for me as they love me so much. Anyway that horrible man Michael Howard is spreading lies about Labour and my beautiful face which he says has had surgery done to it. It's called plastic surgery you idiot!

This morning I got up and had a piece of toast with my wife Cherie who was complaining about not being able to stand the tension of waiting, and that when she becomes Prime Minister she will put a stop to the old age people always getting their own way with everything.

'Excuse me dear but you will never be Prime Minister. If Labour wins I will become the Prime Minister,' I said as if she were trying to take over. But this was one argument she couldn't win!

'Shut up!' she stood up and walked off out the door into the kitchen. A couple of minutes later she realised she had gone the wrong way and stormed off upstairs.

'The votes are in and the winner is ... *Labour!'* the newscaster read aloud with a hint of hatred.

'We did it, we did it, thank you God, drinks all around. Michael Howard is buying!'

Olivia Widdop (12)
Framwellgate School, Durham

A Day In The Life Of Disabled Teenager

Dear Diary,

Today was the worst day of my life. I was involved in a car crash. Some idiot came speeding round the corner in my street, at the last second and rammed into the passenger side of the car, where I was sitting and practically knocked us across the other side of the road.

I was taken into the hospital and was told I could never use my legs properly ever again. No more football, PE, rugby, anything. And the worst thing is, I have to stay in a wheelchair for the rest of my life. I'll have to move to a 'special school' because my school at the moment has no access for the disabled. I still can't get used to saying that; it still hasn't sunk in. I won't be able to walk again. I won't be able to walk again ... ever. I can't understand how people can find joyriding fun. They don't understand that they could really kill or seriously injure someone. Someone like me. I didn't really appreciate the speeding signs and warnings before. I didn't think it would happen to me. I have to go back to the hospital in two weeks' time to check my legs aren't getting any worse, and I am hoping for some good news after today's episode. Anyway, I might talk to you tomorrow. If I survive.

Lauren Kernick (12)
Framwellgate School, Durham

A Day In The Life Of A Person

Once upon a time there was a person called Nula. Nula lived with his parents in a small house in London. He was very rich and he had a very nice servant called William.

One day Nula got very bored so he decided to go on an adventure. He went to a castle called Clem's Castle. When Nula got to the castle he met a king called Phillip. The king said, 'Come Nula and ride my horse,' then Phillip rode a horse as well. The horse bolted and ran away. Nula saved Phillip's life by grabbing the horses' reigns and stopped him from going over the edge of a cliff.

Nula decided to go home. Phillip said it was nice meeting him and to take care. Phillip gave Nula his mobile number so that they could keep in touch. Phillip said, 'You can come any time to visit me. You can bring your family with you.'

Then Nula went, feeling excited and tired from his adventure. When Nula arrived home he told his parents about the great adventure that he had had.

Anum Akbar (15)
Garratt Park School, London

A Day In The Life Of A Mouse

Once upon a time there was a mouse called Mousey. Her mum told her not to go out on her own because it is dangerous, but she didn't listen to her mum.

One morning she got up early and went into the woods. She was scared because she kept on hearing bad noises. She looked up and a big black cat stood in front of her with saliva dripping from its mouth. Its teeth were yellow. Its eyes were glowing like coal burning in the fire. The cat tried to pounce on the little mouse but she managed to get away and ran into a deep hole. She was very scared but she managed to get home and didn't tell her mum, so her mum gave her some cheese. Then she went to bed and she never went in the woods on her own again.

Kirsty Spence (15)
Garratt Park School, London

Sid's Tale

As the sun rose on this fine summer's day the trees swayed dancing in the breeze.

Along the vast park, mothers walked with their children in tow, teenagers laden with books walked onerously towards the distance. An old couple strolled along the path, recalling old memories and dreams for the future. And then there was Sid.

Slumped along the bench like an old rag doll, his hair greasier than an old chip fryer. Shoes tattered and torn, like a ravishing dog had attacked them with his teeth.

Sid sat up, in a drunken daze, he looked around at his surroundings - contemplating his whereabouts and how he'd got there. With his bottle of whiskey still in hand he gathered himself to stand up. Stumbling slightly he took his first step, followed then by him falling flat on his face!

Sid regained himself as he heard the shrill chittering of small girls, he looked up to see the three girls standing there. Clad in raggedy old clothes - more tattered and torn than the old tramp's.

Sid raised his body so it was level with the bench and he carefully placed his aching body on the bench and sat looking directly at the three small girls.

The first girl looked at the small, old, withering tramp and picking an object off the floor she held it up by slowly raising it off the ground.

As she raised the object, Sid saw the shining of metal and the deep colour of red surrounding it.

The knife. Shining with guilty glory - Sid looked at it, his bloodshot eyes tragically gleaming. He stopped for a minute - rethinking the situation.

The girl opened her small mouth and said calmly, 'Sidney Brooks - I'm with the police, you're arrested for murder. You're coming with me.'

Then Sid heard the sirens. He stopped gawping and looked around. He knew he was in trouble.

Archie Burbidge (14)
Harrow Way Community School, Andover

The Flood

I remember the day like it was just yesterday even though a whole year has passed since it happened. At the time I was living in a small Cornish village. The television scared me so much; I refused to believe it was going to happen.

Outside the rain was heavy and I looked out of the window, everything was blurred and the rain showed no sign of stopping any time soon. After a while flash floods and warnings came just minutes too late. The river was already out of hand and it was too late for evacuation. Everyone in the village was on the roofs of the buildings waiting for the rain to stop.

The river, by now, had burst its banks as the constant rain poured out of the sky. Old and weak buildings decayed and were rushed down to the sea.

The river was raging down the hill, ruining and destroying everything it passed causing havoc and pain. Cars floated down the hill, everything inside was being destroyed never to be found again, dogs and belongings lost forever.

It was amazing that everyone managed to get through that day; everyone helped each other to survive and get through the terrible situation. The small village would have never got through it without the amount of community spirit that they had.

Misha New (14)
Harrow Way Community School, Andover

Untitled

Holly woke, dreading the day ahead. She got up yawning and rubbing her eyes. She quickly got washed and dressed, being as silent as she could. Tiptoeing downstairs she started her daily chores.

There was movement upstairs, she knew her mother would have something to say about her waking Lily up.

The baby finally settled down, Holly heard her mum stomping downstairs. 'Sorry Mum; thought I was being quiet,' Holly whispered.

'Obviously not; when you've finished everything down here you can sort Lily out.'

'But I had her while you were out last night.'

'Exactly, that's why I'm going back to bed, do as you're told and don't answer back; you know what you'll get,' her mother said sternly.

Holly did as she was told and carried on, while her mum dragged herself back upstairs. She heard screaming from Lily, she ran upstairs into the baby's room. As she lifted Lily into her arms she flinched in pain as she pressed onto Holly's bruised arms. She rocked her back to sleep gently and returned downstairs.

Later on that day, Holly's mother came into the kitchen where Holly was washing up. She spoke into Holly's ear, stinking of alcohol. 'I'm going out, don't take your eyes off Lily.'

'Mum, I'm tired of this; being the responsible one.'

Holly whimpered as her mother grabbed her hair. 'You'll do as you're told.'

With that she walked out leaving her helpless daughters behind.

Lauren Mennie (14)
Harrow Way Community School, Andover

Tough Times

'For the last time, I said *no!'*

Typical! I've been looking forward to turning 15 for ages! But when I finally do, my parents continue to treat me like a baby! I keep asking Dad for an email address, but he says I'm too young!

Melanie, my best friend, asked whether I wanted to go into town after school today but I dare not say yes as my over protective father makes me be home by 7.30!

Melanie is perfect. She has parents who don't care what she does. She is very pretty, has hair I could die for and is the popular one at school! I'm the complete opposite. I'm short, have thin mousy hair and two of the world's most annoying brothers.

'What's taking you so long Molly?' screams my stepmum up the stairs. 'You're going to be late for school again.'

I manage to drag myself down what seems the never-ending staircase and out the door with, for the second day running, no breakfast.

Melanie is there to greet me wearing a skirt only she could get away with and her silky black hair straightened and looking beautiful. 'Hiya! What happened to you, you look awful.'

Great!

'We've got to hand in our final piece of coursework today. I think I've done OK on it. What about you?'

Just as I thought my day couldn't get any worse, I realise that I've forgotten my coursework! Why does my life seem harder than anyone else's?

Amy Morris (14)
Harrow Way Community School, Andover

A Day In The Life Of A Field Mouse

The sun rose in the east and the glistening rays blazed down, heating the crumbling gavel beneath its petite, fragile feet. Field mouse was scuffling and scrounging, dodging and ducking between the emerald leaves, swerving to miss a dewdrop, slicing through the air like an axe through a tree. Splashing down and seeping down in the cracks in the meadow floor. A cry bellowed out and a whoosh followed.

He looked up. Piercing blue eyes glared down. The blades shone in the light as they clenched together. The kestrel circled the mouse as it scrambled to find a safe haven. He launched himself forward, legs pumping, heart racing as the talons came closer, a hole appeared on the horizon, closer and closer he got to the hole but closer the razor-like claws became too. He sped and skidded into the hole, safe at last.

Sophie Barry (14)
Harrow Way Community School, Andover

Untitled

Planes. Stupidly boring places. On the rare occasions when they give you a TV to watch there's always some out of date film from an obscure country you've never heard of. Then the headphones never work and you experience all sound with an odd hiss so that for the first five minutes of the film you are convinced there is a snake somewhere on board. The magazines shoved in the seat in front of you are from before you were born and the music you listen to is all in Spanish despite the fact that you are neither going to nor leaving anywhere remotely Spanish. Don't get me wrong, I like Spanish music but after the seventeenth song that sounds suspiciously like the third song and surprisingly like the tenth, you do get bored.

Begin the people watching! This is the only thing to do on planes to stop yourself going as barmy as the flight hostesses. The man just across from you with the unrealistically large nose seems to be turning the colour of beetroot, which happens, coincidentally, to be on the menu. There's a lady with an obvious perm and the child with the pigtails who refuses to stop bouncing on her seat, is now being told politely but firmly by an air hostess to 'please, sit, still!' the cracks in her calm vizier growing to great chasms.

Finally, the ordeal over, you get shunted off the plane to either clear skies or classically English rain.

Sophie Walker (14)
Harrow Way Community School, Andover

Was It Real?

Lonely she sat on the high eroded cliff, perched like a butterfly watching over everything that happened down below her. Glancing at the ant-like people walk backwards and forwards along the gravel set path. She then pushed up from her balanced position and stepped back nervously for the crumbling edge.

It wasn't long before she arrived home. She then sat in front of the TV in complete silence. It was so quiet that a penny would be heard if it was dropped. Nothing was said. The doorbell rang. Nothing was done. It rang again. Nothing was done. Then the ringing stopped. She rose from her dreaming state and hobbled to the old, cavern door. As she turned the big brass handle a knocking noise started. She opened the door but no one was there. She could still hear the knocking. It seemed to be getting louder. But no one was there. Then the ringing started again. She slammed the door and ran round the room screaming frantically to cover the sound. Nothing worked. She started banging her head repeatedly against the wall, blood trickling down her battered face and on to her white cotton shirt.

Then it turned back. She couldn't see or hear anything. In the black silence she started to walk but she found nothing. Then she fell to a hard, cold floor and drifted into a deep sleep. No one ever found out what happened to her and she never awoke.

Emma Compton (13)
Harrow Way Community School, Andover

The Fire That Ruined My Life

I don't know why, but I don't think I fit into this family! Every time I look into the fireplace, I get a sudden memory that I can't quite work out.

That night I woke up motionless with the screaming terror in my head. I let it all out. My parents rushed in, asking me what was wrong. I just kept screaming, I couldn't stop.

'Maybe we should tell her,' they said in a quiet whisper. Then my parents walked over to me, the musky warm aroma of their clothes comforted me and I stopped screaming. They told me to relax - they had some news for me, but I couldn't. The strong memory was there and it wouldn't go away. But I listened.

'Emily this may seem confusing to you, but we're not your real parents. Your parents got killed in a fire but luckily you were rescued. There was no hope for your parents. Sorry. We will leave you to think about this,' said my mum, slightly crying. I sank back down into my bed. I felt like all the life inside of me had been sucked out by a giant vacuum.

The next day I knew what I had to do. Find the people who'd killed my mother and father. My mum asked me if I was hungry. I said no. I was too involved to even think about food. Then I found the website. The one about my parents, about their tragic ending ...

Kiree Hotchkin (12)
Harrow Way Community School, Andover

The Life Of Me

Hmmm ... The Life of Me ... what kind of book name is that? But as long as I'm the main character that's all that matters! The name's Splat, Bug, Splat - yes I know what a weird name - Mum's fault. You see I'm a caterpillar nothing more nothing less!

Me and my family of 50 have eaten our home - a nice big plant so I've been told to leave and find us a new place, pah probably just to see if I get eaten! So I've gone. So far I've walked, I mean crawled about 25 centimetres! Woohoo ...

Aww look at that it's a daisy - mmm tasty although I don't like the middle, tastes of ... of bumblebee's bottom! *Yuck!*

'Oh my goodness hide bug buddies, run away, fly away,' screamed a large black beetle stood upon a large rock. Many insects scuttled away - butterflies flew away and woodlice crawled away hiding - but from what? And then a large dark shadow appeared. It loomed overhead. I looked around - the place was deserted. All signs of bug life had disappeared - nothing was left. An eerie breeze blew past me knocking me to one side. Suddenly the shadow dived. I looked up. The mouth of the creature opened - an everlasting dark black hole. I shut my eyes and prayed. *Thud! Squawk!*

I was now trembling. Carefully I opened one eye - yes just one. *'Argh!'*

The thing dropped me! A bird?

I woke up, the sun blinding me, but I was alive, alive I tell you!

Anna Murray (12)
Harrow Way Community School, Andover

The Ghost Train

'Thank you for taking me out tonight!' Bethan said passionately to her hunk.

'That's fine, it's only the London Eye,' Jason replied. 'Come on let's go.'

Jason and Bethan walked hand in hand to the London Eye. All the other carts were full so Jason and Bethan had to go in a cart alone except for one strange man who was largely built.

The strange man started a conversation. 'Hi, I'm Big Max. Beautiful view isn't it?'

'Yes,' Jason replied.

'Have you ever heard of the ghost train down by the subway?'

'No actually I haven't but I would like to,' Bethan said with excitement.

'OK, hold on to your knickers, 3, 2, 1.'

Suddenly Jason, Bethan and Big Max fell through a trapdoor in the cart of the London Eye as soon as they'd reached the top. Big Max shouted to the couple, 'Be careful there are some sharp turns.'

'I'm scared of the dark. Quick Jason hold me,' Bethan yelled.

'It feels like train tracks. Where are we?'

'You are right my friend, we are on the tracks of the ghost train,' replied Big Max.

Suddenly the lights turned on. There was a big mob of what looked like gangsters.

'Hi peeps look who I've brought along, they want to have a go on the ghost train.'

By the time Big Max said that the mob all had smirks on their faces. All of a sudden they heard a loud hoot that sounded like it was coming from a train. Then, slowly creeping around the corner, came the ghost train. Bethan had the look of horror on her face but Jason had the complete opposite. They all got on the ghost train - including the mob.

'Knowing our luck it will break down when it starts to get good.'

Suddenly the ghost train stopped with a shudder and one of the mob punched Jason right in the nose, then dragged him out of the ghost train. They all started kicking and punching him in the stomach, while Big Max held a knife to Bethan's throat.

'Any last words to your beloved boyfriend?' said Big Max.

'Yes I love you Jason.'

'I love you too.'

'Oh I'm so sorry, party's over,' said Big Max.

Jason gave one last kiss before they were separated away into the darkness. All you could hear was the slitting of Bethan's throat and the screaming of her pain.

'You! I hate you. You'll pay for this,' cried Jason.

Two of the mob walked towards Jason and put their hands over his nose and mouth. He struggled and struggled but couldn't get any air. He stopped struggling and there was a short silence in the room.

The next day on the news: 'A couple have been found on an abandoned subway. They were found this morning. Their names were Bethan Dine and Jason Roe. The killer or killers are still on the run. The police are on their case'.

I wonder who will be Big Max's next victim?

Terri Butler & Kayleigh Toms (12)
Harrow Way Community School, Andover

Grass

'I told them. I told them everything. From the attempt to assassinate my father to the way you sent death threats to all of my family in turn ... I, I could kill you,' I cried, my voice slowly rising from a calm, controlled whisper to a full assault on my vocal chords. The huge expanse of body that was slouched in front of me turned and stared straight through me.

'What did you just say?' he grunted, his huge eyes almost popping out of their sockets and rolling across the dusty floor.

'I said I told them! I told the police everything!'

The creature flew across the room, grabbed my throat and shoved me against the exposed brick wall, grazing my shoulder. 'Who would think that a little thing like you would have such a big mouth?'

He squeezed the graze on my shoulder, causing the blood to ooze from within my skin and onto my jeans. He gripped my throat tighter, as if he wanted to force all of the fluids out of my body and onto the floor in front of me. I could not utter a sound. He dug his fingers into my flesh, squeezing all of the life out of me, making me want to collapse. The pain ricocheted off my backbone, like a freshly shot bullet. It flashed from one end of my spine to the other. The lightning bolt had hit its target, and I was it.

'Wait. Let's do this properly.' The greasy man that had inhabited the shadows in the corners since we'd arrived stepped out from the darkness. He held a silver pistol. It glinted in the dim light like a blunt sword belonging to a rogue knight, destined to be thrust into a bleeding heart.

I was right. He raised the pistol and brought it level with my head ...

Hannah Cave (14)
Harrow Way Community School, Andover

24 Hours In The Life Of An African Fly

The distant aroma of cooking aroused me from a sleepless trance. It's an exceptional morning. I can tell.

I haven't eaten properly in days and neither has the African woman and her family. Today we get a meal. I can smell it cooking. The children's eyes could be mistaken for those of famished hawks, tracing the every move of the rice grains as they bounce off each other in a hope to escape the scorching heat.

A sea of outstretched palms are fishing for the rice. The family shovel food into their mouths, clawing at the pot as it is passed round. Desperate for food.

We sit, we wait, rice is no use to us like this. It is too big to eat, so we sit, we wait.

Soon the remains of the rice are smothered around the emaciated faces of tiny children. We no longer sit, we no longer wait, we attack, an army of flies invading the smile-ridden faces of every child while they cry, their stomachs protesting and chanting for food.

After a while, we are full, the onslaught of flies retreats as another attacks. We settle on a nearby cowpat where we observe the scene. As we settle, we clean, lubricating each leg in turn, stretching, like putting on a pair of tights, and finally settling, slipping in and out of sleepless trances.

It was a good day but we won't eat now for days.

Victoria Allmark (14)
Harrow Way Community School, Andover

Untitled

The ground below me began to change colour. I had never been this high before. Darker it became until all around me was grey. Dark grey. I wasn't sure what was about to happen. I had never seen this part of the world. It had taken me days to reach this point, each time I tried I'd fall gracefully back down, so my journey would restart.

I've been many places - Australia, New York, London, Paris. Now I am here. I wasn't sure where I would end up next.

All of a sudden I fell, I kept going. It was too blurry to see where I was. All I could see was other species falling around, all different sizes but all formed the same shape - sharp top points to small round balls. Suddenly I came to a halt - *splat* - on the floor. Now I was even smaller. Parts of me flew around while others joined new communities. I was left alone looking up at other raindrops slowly making their way to the ground. Now it's my time to start again. I've made new friends, parts of me are spread around. I'll never be one again. I begin to rise higher. Let's see how far I make it this time.

Laura Watson (14)
Harrow Way Community School, Andover

The Horizon

'Port turn Teranis, Teranis, I said port turn boy, stop staring at the sky. I know you don't want to be here and frankly I don't want you on my ship either, get to work!' shouted my gruff old captain of this awful ship. He isn't even a real pirate, not even a sailor, he only came into the job for the money. Take a look at his wooden leg, he claims it was taken off by a jet rider, when really a cupboard fell on him. His eye, the one with the patch, he says it got ripped out by a plane's engine when really a doctor said he had bad hay fever and the pathetic attempt for a jet warrior over there hasn't been in a battle since he fought his brother in a cot for his Action Man.

'Boy come here, go up to the crows' nest and look for land.'

'Why?' I replied. 'We're three days from land, you don't need me up there.'

'Just go,' he shouts.

I hate this grumpy old fart. He thinks he rules the world. Huh what's this, it's the moment I realise I am not going to live a second longer! Jet Riders! Hide!

The amazing jets come soaring above my head, like birds in the sky. As I fling myself down the rigging of the ship. They fly over, turn then circle, the ship like sharks looking for a weakness.

The captain loads a cannon and shoots one out of the sky. They soar down and take me by the shoulders like eagles' claws, away into the horizon.

Matthew Baigent (12)
Heathfield Community College, Old Heathfield

Grand Theft Turbo

It all started on the 7th July. A group of car thieves found their final competition, the Ferrari 360.

We smashed through the security station and knocked out the security guard with a crow bar, there it was the Ferrari 360 - red, raging and furious! We snipped through the alarm wire under the hood and threw ourselves into the machine. Suddenly an alarm raged from all around and slowly the warehouse door opened, there was the whole of the Miami police!

We revved the engine, I let go of the clutch and raced over one of the policemen. Seven police cars were chasing us and shooting with pistols. A ramp was in front of me and Christian, but next to it a one hundred foot drop plummeting into the sea! I reversed back and raced the car for the ramp. The car was floating in mid-air. There it was, the other side, the Ferrari began to drop rapidly, were we going to make it? The car thumped against the edge with the back wheels slipping. Frightfully I looked back and a police car was coming right at our car!

It smashed the back of the Ferrari pushing it on the edge, but suddenly the engine blew and was over-revved. The police came from in front and got out of their cars. Christian and I legged it and ran from them, dodging their fragile bullets one by one! We lost them and got back to the hideout where Tom and Matt were modding a Nissan Skyline. It had neon, fat bumpers, side skirts, turbo, roof scoops and finally two giant tanks of nitrogen oxide!

We needed that Ferrari, but how? I had an idea. We drove to the dump yard, when we got there the flames roared from outside! Guard dogs, CCTV, sensors and guards were everywhere. I revved the car and raced through everyone and everything. Christian got out of the car and jumped in the Ferrari. We zoomed side by side, finally there was the entrance, were we gong to make it?

Steven Hancock (12)
Heathfield Community College, Old Heathfield

The Three Mice Go West

In an ordinary town in Mexico, there were three ordinary Mexican mice. They lived in a town called Moricado. Their home was in an old Mexican pub, in a little hole in the corner of the old shack. Their names were El Diablo, the eldest, Moresesa and Pete, the youngest.

'This is boring,' moaned El Diablo.

'There's nothing in this town, no nice food, no good-looking girls and no cheese!' groaned Pete.

'We need to get away from this ghost town,' suggested Moresesa.

'But where to?' El Diablo questioned.

'Wild West?' asked Pete.

'Mmm ...' El Diablo said softly.

'I've heard that it's got everything,' Pete replied.

'How are we going to get there?' Moresesa asked.

'We'll go by horse, well donkey, but near enough!' Pete instructed.

'We will leave tonight,' El Diablo decided.

That night they left for the Wild West, so excited they didn't take anything to eat.

'I'm hungry!' Moresesa moaned.

'Should have thought of eating before we went,' El Diablo replied.

They arrived at midnight. They had nowhere to sleep apart from a butcher's shop.

'This is great!' Moresesa said, sarcastically.

'This will have to do,' Pete said back.

'Besides this is just the beginning,' El Diablo said reassuringly.

In the morning they looked for food everywhere, when they came across an old rat.

'Hey, where's all the food?' Pete glared at the rat.

'There has been no food for weeks since the Kung Fu cats took the beloved Sheriff Wigum,' mumbled the old rat.

'We must do something,' El Diablo said.

'The reward is 1,000,000kg of cheese,' the rat said.

They decided to go.

Sebastien Ryall (11)
Heathfield Community College, Old Heathfield

The Man Who Betrayed His Country

I slowly crawled through the undergrowth of the woods, close to the castle I was meant to be spying on, Pevensy Castle. A cart of swords and armour was slowly pulled past by a sick, dreary-looking donkey. Maybe the English knew that we French were planning an attack, no they couldn't have found out. I was just about to try and sprint into the castle. I quickly ran, luckily no one saw me. The guards in the battlements must have been incredibly tired from last night's drinking contest. My next task was to find a secret place.

There were plenty of secret places hidden in the towering battlements above my head, but none of them good enough. I needed a really secret place. Out of the corner of my eye I saw a small rotting trapdoor, quite close to the moat. I walked over and tried to lift it up, and with a bit of luck it slowly creaked open. I peered down, the only noise was the dripping of water. I slowly clambered down. It seemed like the room was a forgotten dungeon. There was an awful smell of decay looming in the air, the walls were slowly crumbling away leaving patches of damp mud. This is where I was going to have my secret hideout.

The first thing I had to do was to write a letter to the French saying where my secret hideout was and also tell my countrymen where to attack. When I'd come running to the castle, I had seen a stream of sewage leading through a rusting grate and into the moat. That is where they should plant the gunpowder.

I decided to come out of my hiding place and just have a stroll around the small village within the castle's almighty walls. There were all sorts of different market stalls; armouries, pens, parchments and clothes. When I walked along the streets there was a horrible smell of poo and the air smelt stale and stagnant. I bought a new feather pen, a roll of parchment and then went back to my hideout.

When I returned there were quite a few footprints all over the grimy floor, but that was of no concern to me. I opened the trapdoor and climbed into the chamber. I heard a few voices outside and I began to get worried. I didn't know what to do, there was no way out apart from the way in. I was trapped in my own plan. Suddenly men came running in armed with swords and muskets, one of them fell down the steps, obviously he was fat and clumsy! The leader was a bulky man wearing rusting armour with dents engraved in it from previous battles. It looked like he had lost them as he had loads of scars on his face. One eye was patched up. 'I think you'll be coming with me,' he snarled.

It became clear that I had been knocked out as I had an egg-shaped bruise bulging out the side of my head. I looked around and in the misty darkness there were all kinds of torture tools covered in blood. My heart began to beat faster and faster. A small crippled man came out from the darkness and pulled one of the tools off the wall. 'I'm going to enjoy torturing you until you give in to writing reply letters to the French leading them to the wrong place.' He began to cut me all over, I managed to withstand the first few slashes but eventually I gave in to the pain.

'Alright, I will obey your orders!' I began to write the letters with a shaky hand that was betraying my country and sacrificing thousands of lives. When I finished the man pulled me away into a jail cell.

The ambush took place at about 4 o'clock in the afternoon. I was there watching the massacre with my hands and legs clamped together and a guard by my side. The French were slaughtered like dogs. You could hear the clash of blade against blade from miles away. The battle was a great victory for the English, so they thought. Later, after the battle, I was taken back to my jail cell to live there for the rest of my miserable life.

Edward Koops (12)
Heathfield Community College, Old Heathfield

The Ghost Of Gawk Street!

'Aw, this house is lovely,' Sarah said to her daughter, Laura.

They had just moved to a huge house on Gawk Street.

'Right,' Laura said to her mother, 'I'm going to see if I can make any new friends.' She marched out of the door and made her way to a few houses. Then she stopped. Right next to her was a big house with broken windows and a torn door. Laura ran up and knocked on it. 'Hello?' she cried. 'Is there anybody in?' She wanted to make sure everyone was okay so she stumbled in and looked through a few of the rooms. In the lounge, there was torn wallpaper everywhere and the furniture was all pushed over.

Just then, she heard a noise coming from upstairs. Laura ran up and burst in one of the rooms. 'Aarrgghh!' she screeched.

There was an old lady lying on the floor with bones sticking out of her arms and blood dripping down from her head. Laura ran all the way back to her house.

She couldn't find her mum anywhere. But when she ran into the bathroom and looked into the bath, Sarah was lying there with scratches all up her legs and blood dripping down her ears.

Suddenly, there was a big bang from downstairs. Laura hurried down and when she got to the kitchen, she saw a pale man in a top hat looking down at her.

She picked up a china plate and threw it at him. To Laura's surprise, it went straight through his head. He was a ghost! He grabbed Laura's arms and twisted them so the bones turned. Then he stuck a knife in her throat. She was dead.

Jasmin Humphrey (12)
Heathfield Community College, Old Heathfield

The Girl Who Wasn't Scared ... Until Now!

'Of course the wood isn't haunted, that's just a load of rubbish, who have you been talking to Cath? Honestly!' Lizzie laughed looking at Cath.

'No one, I mean everyone knows that it's haunted, you're so stupid!' replied Cath.

'Fine then, if you think I'm stupid then I'll prove to you it isn't haunted, you just watch, I'm not scared of some silly tale!' Lizzie cried as she stormed off to the edge of the dark woods.

As she got nearer though a small shiver ran down her back but she ignored it and carried on. Suddenly she realised where she was. While she had been lost in her thoughts she had reached the gate leading to the woods. *I must be strong,* she thought, so she stood tall and opened the gate. Her feet made gentle crunching sounds as she softly padded through the broken twigs and fallen leaves. Ahead of her she saw a sparkling stream so she quickly ran towards it. But, when she got to where she thought it was she stared round in horror, there was nothing there, not even a tiny drop of water let alone a whole stream. *I must be going mad,* she thought. Then she heard a voice in the distance.

'Lizzie, Lizzie, Lizzie, come over here Lizzie, I know you're scared Lizzie.'

'How d-d-do you kn-kn-know my name? Who ar-ar-are you?' stuttered Lizzie shaking and shivering.

'I'm coming over to you Lizzie, I'm looking right at you Lizzie, can't you see me?'

Lizzie quickly backed away screaming loudly and tripped on a tree root, she hastily tried to get up but something was pinning her to the ground.

'Don't go Lizzie, please stay Lizzie, I want you to stay.'

Andrea Beach (12)
Heathfield Community College, Old Heathfield

Britain Or Rome?

Marcipias woke up. The officer who woke him quietly explained to him the situation. He dressed and buckled on his short sword. Marcipias climbed slowly onto the turf ramparts, still fumbling with his shield strap. The cold British wind swept through him. Marcipias shivered and peered over the battlements. They were down there. He turned around. The eyes of his cohort peered up anxiously at him. Marcipias nodded. 'Celts!'

The cohort leapt onto the ramparts just in time. The Celts swept up with a roar, dashing into the waiting Romans. Marcipias hacked at the rabble. He glanced sideways, Marcipias, second in command, Maray was on the gate. Grimly he clasped his sword with a sweaty palm and rejoined the fray. One large Celt threw himself at Marcipias, his shield was torn from his grasp, his shoulder popped. He leapt aside and slashed at the advancing swarm, pain shooting up his arm. Marcipias winced. Vailair, a loyal friend stumbled towards him, glaring a quick grin. Another Celt, screaming like a banshee, brought his sword down on Vailair. Choking with rage, Marcipias stabbed the Celt.

'Cavalry!' an officer cried as the reinforcements poured in.

Marcipias walked up to Aqiula, the camp commando. Aqiula sneered.

'So time to leave.'

Marcipias didn't want to, his friends had died in this country. 'No.'

'If you don't leave the Celts will kill you!'

Marcipias knew otherwise. He threw his armour at Aqiula, dumped his sword, and ran towards a village, letter the mist swallow him.

Alexander Morris (12)
Heathfield Community College, Old Heathfield

Party Popper

'But Mum, why won't you let me go? Everyone else is; Sarah, James and Nick are all going, it's so unfair!' So I marched upstairs, slamming my door shut, hoping Mum would come apologising but all she said was, 'You are not going to that party'. I knew she would say no, but I was going to that party, no matter what she said.

Later that night, I tied up several sheets to make a rope, then threw it out of my bedroom window and climbed to where my friends were waiting for me.

'Come on before your mum hears us,' moaned Nick.

Off we went to Club Diva.

When we arrived it was packed with wild party animals; I was a bit nervous but I was with my friends. I took a deep breath and entered. Little did I know in a few minutes we would all be in deep trouble. Then it happened, just like that the room was filled with water; everyone screaming, a table floated past, I tried to grab hold of it but missed. My whole life flashed before me, I screamed but I was not heard, was I going to die?

There was nothing I could do but just when I thought all was lost I saw a face, it was James. I can't remember much of what happened after that, all I can say is that was the worst day of my life. I have never disobeyed Mum since.

Jessica Hollyman (11)
Heathfield Community College, Old Heathfield

The Big Game!

'Zzzz,' on a Sunday morning.

'Wake up!' shouted my mum.

I rose from my pit.

'It's my final today!' I screamed, I literally jumped into my tennis clothes, ran downstairs, scoffed my breakfast, raced for the car. I whizzed down the road. *Disaster!* 'My racquets!' I screeched to a halt. My match was at 9am sharp or I had to forfeit the match. The clock said 8.57. Could I make it in time? I zoomed home, grabbed my racquets and literally flew back to the club. 8.59, I parked and ran on court, just in time for the match.

We started the match - 0-0. The first game went to me 1-0. His serve whizzed past me. 'Ace!' he shouted. For the rest of that game I may as well have not been there. He aced me again, and again and again. 1-1. I never give in. I served, he returned and I smashed the ball. Oops! The ball hit him in the middle of the forehead with a wallop! I ran over to the other side of the net and apologised so much I collapsed. He couldn't hear. He was knocked unconscious. My mum called an ambulance and it arrived in no time.

They picked him up and lay him on a stretcher in the van. He was taken to hospital and treated there. He forfeited the match but I felt bad.

My mum said, 'It's not your fault, you were just playing tennis.'

I asked his mum to let us know how he was getting on but she didn't phone and tell us for ages. I then realised that I hadn't given her my phone number, so I went to see him. As I went in, he was skipping out of the doors, fine - thankfully!

Tommi Caldwell (12)
Heathfield Community College, Old Heathfield

Quake In The Quarry

One warm, summer's day, John and his friends were on an 'off road' bike ride, when they stumbled upon an unused quarry. They started showing each other tricks and seeing who could jump the highest. As John approached the ramp, he pedalled as fast as he could. His body filled with adrenaline. He soared higher than anyone else, the moment seemed to last forever.

Unfortunately, the landing didn't go as planned. He crashed into the bank, it collapsed, trapping his leg. John moaned for help, realising he was unable to move. His friend held up his mobile phone and shouted, 'Don't worry, I'll call for help.' He tried to phone his mum, but the annoying voice of the woman telling him that he had no credit rung in his ears. Rob remembered that he could call an emergency service. 'Help me please, my friend is stuck at the bottom of Pembrooke Quarry, his leg is trapped, we need some help, please.' Rob struggled to control the fear in his voice.

'Don't worry,' the lady at the other end of the phone said reassuringly, 'help is on its way.'

The following half hour seemed like a lifetime to both John and Rob. They awaited the familiar sound of an ambulance approaching, but nothing arrived. Suddenly the sky seemed to get darker and a loud roaring noise came closer and closer. It was a rescue helicopter!

After a short stay in hospital and his broken leg plastered for 6 weeks, John was soon back on his bike, but now was careful not to create a 'quake in the quarry'!

James Davies (12)
Heathfield Community College, Old Heathfield

Dragon Boy

The great beast glided through the night air as silent as the wind, upon it was the greatest warrior of all time. In the warrior's arms was a bundle, the bundle was a baby.

The warrior put the baby at the front of a little hut. The baby was a little boy, he had fair blond hair and eyes as black as charcoal; around his neck was a great gift, as sharp as a sword and as strong as a diamond ... a dragon claw.

'Freak! Skimpy little freak! Come on! Give us your best shot!'

Dracon lunged out with his right fist and clipped Crodun on the nose.

'You call that a punch,' Crodun mocked, 'that was a poke! Did your useless blacksmith of a father teach you that?'

Crodun's crude friends sniggered in the background.

Dracon got annoyed, no one called *his* father useless. His father was the best blacksmith in the kingdom. None could make stronger shields, lighter armour or sharper swords; Crodun would pay. 'You'll pay for that!' Dracon threatened. He punched Crodun in the mouth then his guts.

'Not bad ... but not good enough,' said Crodun as his fist swung through the air.

Dracon slashed again and hit Crodun in the temple. Crodun fell to the floor as Dracon jumped on him. He couldn't control himself as the anger welled up inside Dracon. 'I'll smash and rip you to bits!' screamed Dracon as he clawed at Crodun's face.

Crodun's stooges watch as Dracon attacked their leader but they didn't dare help. They were too scared ... Dracon had changed. His skin looked tough with a green shine, his ears became a small hole with spikes on the back, his eyes turned an evil red, the back of his head had protruding horns and his mouth and face were longer and thinner.

Dracon got up to see everyone flinching and looking away. He looked at his hands, they were green and hard and his nails had become talons.

Crodun backed away looking horrified and mumbled something under his breath. 'What are you?'

Dracon turned and fled to the forest. He ran for hours, calming down all the way and changing back. After a while of running Dracon came to a clearing and rested. *What happened back there?* thought Dracon as he walked.

Eventually he came across a cave in the ground and went down to find some shelter.

'Greetings, Dracon,' said a voice in the gloom.

'Who's there?' Dracon asked. 'How do you know my name?'

The voice answered, 'I was a warrior but now I am a wizard, my name is Acholli and I know what's happened to you, I can help you; come with me!'

Dracon panicked, 'No! It's a trap, go away! I'm going home, leave me alone!'

'Are you sure that's wise? Your village think that you are dangerous, they won't accept you. I can help you,' said Acholli as he stepped into the light, he had a long grey beard, great robes and soft light blue eyes. 'I can tell you what's happening.'

Dracon turned around and looked into his eyes and faintly he saw a glimmer of trust. He said the one thing that had been on his mind the whole time, 'What am I?'

Dan Hilton & Olly Stredwick (12)
Heathfield Community College, Old Heathfield

The Lake

(An extract)

Alex was thirteen years old, all his life he'd been told to stay away from the lake. His mum and dad would never let him anywhere near it, that whole section of the garden was out of bounds. The last person to swim in that pond was Alex's brother Mark and he never came back. He was sucked under by a powerful undercurrent; they never even found his body, the lake was so vast and deep. Alex had never met his brother, he'd died while Alex's mum was pregnant and perhaps if Alex had met him Alex wouldn't have done what he did that night. But you cannot dwell on past mistakes.

Alex didn't even know why he did it; it was like his legs were moving themselves, closer and closer to his probable death. As Alex slid his legs into the lake he was amazed by the texture of it, if silk were liquid this is what it would be. He scooped up some of the water and drank, it tasted as sweet as honey but as refreshing as the best water. Alex couldn't resist, he slipped himself into the pond and swam to the centre, it was lovely! There was no danger at all, it couldn't be more enjoyable, and that was when it happened. A powerful current gripped Alex and dragged his head underwater, he started to panic, he didn't deserve to die! He struggled to get back above the water but it only slowed his descent. Alex's lungs were burning, he couldn't hold his breath for much longer, every muscle in his body was aching. Then the pain eased, he saw his own body as though through somebody else's view looking down on him. *This must be death,* Alex thought. Suddenly, two cold hands gripped Alex's arm and yanked him up, up through the surface of the water. *It must be Dad,* Alex thought, *Dad has come to save me.* Alex opened his eyes and peered into the face of his rescuer, it wasn't Dad, it was an old man, incredibly old with a white beard. Alex looked around, he didn't recognise any of his surroundings, this wasn't his garden. He looked back to the old man who said just four words, 'You must be Alex.'

'Are you God?' Alex asked, it was the only thing he could think of saying.

The old man laughed. 'I'm not God, my name is Lake Watcher, Mark has told me you would come.'

Alex stared back dumbly, could this Mark be his brother?

'Perhaps I should start at the beginning,' the old man said. 'First of all I congratulate you on being the second human ever to travel between the two worlds, the first being your brother Mark. This lake is the only gateway we know of and it is my job to make sure nothing passes through except for things that must. This world used to be like yours, a long time ago, before the virus. Like yours, our civilisation was dependent on computers so when someone made a virus that wiped every hard drive on the planet, all banks collapsed, governments crumbled, and the world was thrown back into the dark ages. The strong lived off the weak and did whatever they liked without police to stop them. Eventually, the world was divided into five realms controlled by warlords who were constantly at war with each other. After 500 years one family of warlords conquered the rest, creating the first global empire. However, ever since the warlords came to be, there has been a resistance, and I am proud to say that I am a member of that resistance. The rebel camp was set up a few hundred metres away from this deserted lake, but during its construction the builders discovered a bottle containing a prophesy that two boys named Mark and Alex would come out of the lake and lead the resistance to victory!'

The old man, or Lake Watcher, was smiling enthusiastically. Alex felt sick. He wasn't sure what he believed. He believed that something seriously weird had happened but he didn't believe he had come to a different world and he certainly didn't believe his brother was still alive somewhere. Alex agreed to let Lake Watcher lead him through the forest around the lake to the rebel base, at least he seemed friendly. Then it hit Alex, he must be dreaming, yes that was it. At least he hoped it was ...

Toby Crisford (12)
Heathfield Community College, Old Heathfield

Over The Top

On the battlefields of World War I a generation of young men was tragically wiped out. This is an account about one of these men. This man was Russian.

The Tsar Nicholas II declared war on Germany and Austria and became an ally of Britain and France. The first Russian battle was in Eastern Prussia. General Pavel Rennenkampf's First Army launched an assault on the German Eighth Army commanded by General Friedrich von Prittwitz. Two days later General Alexander Samsonov's Second Army attacked the right flank of the Germans. I was in that very attack.

'Over the top!' shouted the brigadier.

The scene that greeted us was worse than the sewer-like trenches. Everything was dead, two days of fighting had seen to that and there were the enemy, the reason my vast, beautiful homeland was now nothing but dead trees and scorched blackened grass. At that very moment blood surged through my head and I charged forward. The Germans did not know what had hit them. Two days fighting had already demoralised them, our attack was the final blow. When we crashed into their serried ranks I was hit by a rifle bullet in the arm, my arm was shattered. From where I lay all I could see was the smoke of battle. Soon out of the mist came the medics to take me to first aid, so I'll live to fight another day. But many will not again fight for our great country, Russia.

Alexander Rowlatt (12)
Heathfield Community College, Old Heathfield

Future Kid

Deep in space, far away from their home planet of Kapash, the starship Vulture was on red alert.

'Help, we have lost all power except the escape pods,' shouted the engineer in the control room.

The escape pods shot out of the ship Vulture just before it blew up. The Korgs blew them all up, except one. The one with a 15-year-old boy called Black. He threw the switch to go at its top speed and went back in time.

On Earth, a young boy called Tom was lying in his front garden next to the forest. He was 10 years old and full of a lot of energy. He was just going back when he saw a blinding flash and turned around to see this pod-like thing falling out of the sky. It had a flame of fire coming out of the back and was aiming for the forest. Tom was spinning between the trees, leaping over logs until he reached it. He was surprised what an impact it had made. A 10m circle of dying flames was around the pod. He had never seen anything like it. He walked up to it. He thought it would be hot, but he touched it anyway. It was cold, deathly cold. *Hiissss.* Tom jumped back. A door was opening and a bright light was shining out. When it was fully open, there stood a boy. A boy that would start a new beginning for Tom. A boy from the future.

'Hello there,' said Black. 'Nice place. It's good to be on Kapash again.'

'What! This is Earth, not Kapash,' said Tom. 'What do you think I am. Mad!'

Then it struck Black. He was on the same planet, but back when they called it Earth. 'What's your name?' said Black.

'Tom Catch.'

This couldn't be true. This was his great, great, great, great, great, grandad. The greatest inventor in history ...

Alex Crump (12)
Heathfield Community College, Old Heathfield

Evil Eye In Godworld

Set in the rolling countryside of Godworld. The green rolling hills with sheep grazing on the side. Picturesque houses set in the hills. Rivers running through the hills, cattle, sheep, horses grazing round the little villages. You could hear nothing but the rustle of trees and bushes.

One day there was a god called Zeus who kept everyone under control down on Earth. One day Zeus got ill so he left the god of evil in charge of Earth.

The next day everything was going fine until lunchtime. They all went to eat in a restaurant every day and two men started to fight about who would have the last roll. The two men were Robbie and Connor. The god of evil encouraged them to fight but Connor died.

Everything seemed to be going downhill after the fight, all the plants and animals died. All the houses crumbled away and windows smashed into a thousand pieces! Zeus' illness got worse day by day and more things seemed to die! More people were dying, all buildings set alight. You could not picture the peaceful scenery anymore! All the rolling hills were on fire. The only good thing that was happening was that Zeus was getting better! Day by day he became stronger, the world became more peaceful, like it should be.

Just a bit more than a week after Zeus had recovered the whole place was back to normal.

Hannah Pomfret (11)
Heathfield Community College, Old Heathfield

One Minute It Was There, The Next It Was Gone

The storm was throwing the waves of the sea up onto Burnt Oak Cottage. The lightning struck the trees outside in the old, neglected garden and Katie was comforting her little sister as she cried her eyes out wishing the storm would stop.

Katie herself loved the storm and loved all storms for that matter. She was born in a storm and lived right by the sea where storms were at their worst.

Katie put her sister to bed and looked out the misty window. There out on the vicious sea was a ship. The ship was a large, what looked to be, a pirate ship. This pirate ship also flew the flag of a skull and crossbones.

No one was at home with Katie and her sister. Her mum and dad had gone out to a friend's birthday party. Katie thought the ship had disappeared, she couldn't find it anywhere, maybe it was a ghost ship.

Katie ran down the stairs and out onto the pier that stood over the shore. Water sprayed in her face and the taste of salt was unstoppable. She looked everywhere, all over the ocean until she could see no further. The ship was gone.

The storm carried on through the night and Katie couldn't sleep. She got out of bed and sleepily walked to her own window.

With a flash of lightning the ship appeared and with another flash the ship vanished once more.

Alice Hellowell (11)
Heathfield Community College, Old Heathfield

The Show

'We are here,' shouted Hannah, it was the day of Berryford Horse Show. Hannah and her family were unloading ...

'Hannah go and get Tamtam ready,' shouted Hannah's mum from inside the car.

Hannah unloaded Tamtam, put on his tack, then mounted. 'Mum I'm ready!' she shouted.

'What is your first event?' she replied.

'Showjumping.'

Five minutes later Hannah was ready to enter the ring.

'Please could Hannah Sear and Tamtam enter the ring to start jumping. But first some info on both horse and rider. Hannah is 12 years old and has been riding for 4 years. Tamtam is a 13hh Welsh B gelding and she is 7 years old. Okay and on my call go. Off you go. And they're off, going over 1 then 2 then ...'

'Aarrgghh!'

In an instance Hannah was on the floor as Tamtam galloped out of sight. Soon the ambulance came, Hannah was checked over, she was alright but she had sprained her wrist. Luckily a nearby watcher had caught Tamtam, Hannah, her mum and Tamtam headed back to the trailer then home.

A week later Hannah received a letter through the post, it said that she was going to take part in the showjumping in Olympia in November. Her dream had come true. They would have to jump 4 foot but that wouldn't matter.

Emily Lucas (11)
Heathfield Community College, Old Heathfield

A Day In The Life Of A Coin

I am a coin wohoo, I am in someone's pocket, I think, oh, ow the person must be running round a lot. My head hurts, I feel dizzy. Stop it.

I am sliding along but why, oh that's right I saw those things when I went shopping with my dad, they are called um, conveyor belts, that's it. Why have I stopped? I am being picked up. I can see the ceiling of the shop, but why? His ugly sweaty hands have picked me up so that has answered one of my questions. Why has he dropped me on the floor? Ow, my head.

Where am I? Why is it pitch-black? Why am I asking you? And, ow, my head. *Beep.* I hear a cash register and another one and another. Then out of nowhere the tray I am in opens and I feel sick. Another hand. Leave me alone! God, wash your hands for once. Why am I always being picked up? Oh great I am in someone's palm. Oh God, why me?

It's dark, too dark, where am I? Someone help! What is on me? It is all sticky. *Someone help me.* Oh, thank you Lord, and who is this knight in shining armour? *Hello,* pick this chewing gum off me please. It is really disturbing me.

Oh, fine ignore me then. OK let's go through this again. I am in someone's pocket with gum stuck to me and now I am stuck to his pocket, oh great!

Georgie Earland (12)
Heathfield Community College, Old Heathfield

The War-King Returns

The Black Death they called it. Nobody came out alive, only one person had even come out and that was as a skeleton. That was where Ragbah was now. He had heard (as a captain) that foul beasts were flying out of the Black and destroying nearby settlements. Apparently a pheasant had seen a war-king on the back of one of these terrible beasts. Ragbah was amazed when he had heard this, he thought all the war-kings were wiped out thousands of years ago. Back then the war-kings reigned, but not this time. Ragbah would have to make his move soon.

There was a massive gate by two black cliffs. Ragbah's friend (an elf) came by his side, his name was Gegoraras.

'How are we going to get past that?' enquired Gegoraras.

'We have some Trebuchet coming soon,' answered Ragbah, 'those gates will crumble like dry earth.'

'The Trebuchet have arrived Captain Ragbah,' called out a rider.

'Well let's get going then,' Ragbah ordered.

Everybody stood in place and the riders got ready to charge.

'Fire the Trebuchet!' screamed Ragbah. *Boom! Crash! Boom!* All the boulders slammed into the gate crushing it immediately.

'Charge!' shouted the captain. 'Give them no mercy.'

Men dressed from head to foot in black armed with spears and swords came running from the Black. Everybody started running and shouting, hacking the enemy to pieces. Then suddenly a terrifying scream came from over their heads.

'Dragons!' screamed Ragbah. 'Gegoraras, get your men out of there.'

But it was too late. They came swooping and killing all in their path. Then one saw Ragbah. It widened its terrible jaws and roared in his face before ripping his head off.

James Cole (12)
Heathfield Community College, Old Heathfield

Run Away Corgi!

Have you ever done something amazing? I did last week and now I am a famous heroine, just like that!

It was a lazy Sunday morning and I was reading the newspaper when suddenly I spotted a section, on the Queen's pet corgi, now it's not every day you hear about the Queen's dog is it? So I was entranced to read it. It turned out that her precious pet had run away and there was a £1,000 reward for anyone who found it and brought it back safely. It also said that it had been last seen running over a bridge towards the London Eye.

I jumped up and grabbed my explorer's rucksack that I'd got for Christmas, it came with an abseiling rope and a safety helmet.

I had been waiting to do something fantastic all my life and now here was my chance staring at me in black and white. The London Eye was not far from my house so I set out to find the runaway pooch!

I was just crossing the bridge near the Eye when I heard people gasping. I looked up and there standing near the Eye was a large group of people staring at the top of it. I noticed something else, the London Eye had been stopped!

Suddenly I heard a bark, I looked up and there on the top of the London Eye was ... the Queen's dog! But it was not in one of the pods, oh no it was on top of the highest pod.

'What do we do?' said a woman with a buggy.

'Move over,' I said. I grabbed my rope. Using it like a lasso I threw one end onto a metal bar near the pooch. I climbed up the rope, grabbed the dog and abseiled down. Just like that I became a celebrity.

Holly Mawer (12)
Heathfield Community College, Old Heathfield

A Casual Trip To The Cinema

'Come on, we're going to be late!' shouted Mel, up the stairs.

I ran out of the bathroom, checking that I looked completely casual. My brown hair, was gelled up in a fauxhawk, as it always is. My T-shirt, red, looked just as normal, loose and baggy. I hoped she wouldn't notice that I'd showered for the occasion. I mean, I don't fancy her or anything. We're friends, going to the cinema for a casual movie. The movie, 'The Curse of the Evil Mummy', a fabulously scary, funny and romantic film.

'Ah, Isaac has finally risen. Come on, we'll be late!'

We got there to see a mass of people lined up.

'This is a waste of time; I'm going home.'

'No!' Mel protested, shaking her head.

I watched her long, brown silky hair in a trance and found myself nodding my head. 'Come on. We line up, watch the film, get scared, go home, get changed, get a kebab. Simple, now come on!'

Somehow I bought tickets and sat down on a seat in one swish of hair.

Three hours, several drinks and a few trips to the toilet later, we were leaving the cinema feeling extremely disappointed or, at least I was. I was meant to look like a hero. Instead I'd jumped up and hid behind my popcorn more than Mel. At one point, someone tapped on my shoulder to see if I could please move. I screamed and ran to the toilet. The funny parts, Mel said, didn't compare with a few of my antics. If she had to laugh, it should be *with* me, not *at* me.

'Come on, let's go and get a kebab. Last one there has to pay!'

Upon reflecting on my time at the cinema, I saw that it's me Mel likes, not the heroic, brave person I tried to be. I just had to be myself.

Christo Tsilifis (12)
Heathfield Community College, Old Heathfield

Green Avenue

The rain hammered down onto the empty street, it was strange to see no one on the streets at this time of evening. There's normally drunken teenagers, throwing up all over the place and singing at the tops of their voices, and yet it seemed that there were no drunken teenagers or merry adults going to the toilet at the side of the road. This was uncanny for Green Avenue!

There was a mysterious man leaning against a wall, outside a pub, he looked as if he were waiting for someone, but they hadn't come.

He was half lit up by the yellow, glaring street lamps, his staring eyes fixed upon one thing, the pub door, his glasses reflected the light back at anyone who looked at him, no one knew who he was, but they knew this was an eerie sight.

The pub door opened and the strange man disappeared into the night. It was a young man who had just come out of the door, he had dark hair and was skinny. A mysterious figure snuck up behind the young man and took him by the neck. A great scream was heard, a high-pitched wailing, and a thud.

The next day the young man was found dead, no marks from a fight, no cuts, no drugs. But he was dead and no one knew how or why he had died.

Ben Wickens (12)
Heathfield Community College, Old Heathfield

Sarlina

When the important gods had been made, when the wicked demons had been invented, the gods were called The Almighty Lords. Neler was the Emperor of them, Dillsing was the powerful leader of the Seapans. The Seapans were a terrifying army of evil demons. They had fought against the villagers five years ago.

A girl in a village was called Sarlina. There are many stories about her. This is one of them.

She was the kindest person in the village but she didn't know her past. One amazing night she was sitting on a chair looking out of a window. Just then a bright light shone in the dark sky. Sarlina moved away from the light, covering her eyes, but the gigantic light caught her and Sarlina disappeared into the air like fire that goes out.

She landed on the ground softly and calmly and found herself in an enjoyable place where souls can be safe. 'Welcome back, Sarlina,' said a lovely voice.

'Who are you and where am I?' shouted Sarlina, going round like a spinning top. Her questions went round the space like it was a cradle.

'I am Neler, the Emperor of the heavens, and you are in Heaven,' answered Neler.

Sarlina suddenly realised she was wearing a beautiful white dress instead of a dirty brown one.

'You don't know what you are, do you?' questioned Neler, as he reappeared in front of Sarlina. 'You had to go down to Earth because of the demons from the terrible place. We had to evacuate all the young and you were the youngest. You went to the village. Now you are home and completely safe. Now you are a good and powerful angel floating in the gorgeous air. You are safe.'

Ben Strong (13)
Herons Dale (Special) School, Shoreham-by-Sea

Hiawatha's Hideout

All my friends went to this land of Hiawatha. He said to us, 'What are you doing on my land?'

I said, 'Hiawatha, can you take us to your hideout?'

He said, 'First you and your friends have to do a task. There's a fire and you have to go on a lion's back and juggle with balls and when you finish it you and your friends can go to my hideout.'

We did all this and Hiawatha took us there. It was flames of fire and the arrow maker appeared. He said to me, 'Do you want to buy an arrow?'

There was a great wind and rain and we all ran to the hideout. Nacomis said to Hiawatha, 'Can I sing a song to you?'

We all sat down and listened. 'Yo, yo, wi, ha, yo, yo, wi, ha, ha, ya, ya, ku, ku, rich garden.'

There was a light of fire and the west wind came down and the wind sped across Hiawatha's hideout and it roared ...

Jesse Whyte (12)
Herons Dale (Special) School, Shoreham-by-Sea

The Mystery Of Treasure

Once upon a time there was a prince and his name was William and the king had asked him to go and find some treasure, so they started their journey to find the treasure. The followers were going along when they suddenly had to cross over a river and they had a rope to help them, so they went on with their journey.

That night they were tucked up in bed and they were ready for sleep. Next morning they all got up early and continued their journey. They were really tired and as they were walking along one of the followers said, 'I've just heard a voice and I feel very scared.'

One of the other followers said, 'Don't worry, we're here to look after you if you get scared.'

So they went on with their journey. They came to a place which was very dark and in some light they saw a chest. They went up to it and looked inside and they saw gold and the followers said, 'We are looking for treasure.'

'Oh,' said another follower, 'we've found it. We'd better start getting back to His Majesty.'

They all got back to the camp and had something to eat and when that went down they all went to bed. Next morning they went to His Majesty and said, 'Majesty, I have some good news. I have found your treasure.'

'Well done,' said His Majesty. 'I knew I could trust you. For doing all your journey, getting the treasure and coming back, you lot deserve a medal each.'

Sophie Mussell (12)
Herons Dale (Special) School, Shoreham-by-Sea

The Story Of Joey

One day some people decided to go on holiday on the plane but the plane broke down and crashed and only some people were saved. A child called Joey smashed the plane door and jumped out and looked around.

He had a good idea for building a home. He made a home out of sticks and built it well: he got some really big leaves and made two holes each side and hung them up, and then Joey made some weapons.

Joey saw two people coming. The people said, 'Do you live here?'

'I'm not telling you,' said Joe, 'because you are strangers.'

Joey got some rope and tied it to the door, jumped on the rope, swung on it and knocked the villains on the foot. Joey jumped off and landed on a dragon. The villains got up and started running but it was too late, the dragon was all ready.

With Joey on the dragon it flew away to a magical land. Later Joey tied a leaf to a stick and made a fishing rod and went fishing. He caught 6 fish. He put the fish on the floor, got some wood, found some matches, lit the fire and cooked the fish to eat.

The next morning he woke up and saw a dragon in front of him. He got on the dragon but when he was up in the air he saw two villains behind him, following the dragon and him. He looked down and saw a castle. He looked up and saw the villains from a distance. He went into the castle and said to himself, 'The villains are coming this way because they are coming to look for the dragon.'

Joey made a bow and arrow and when the villains knocked at the castle door they said, 'Have you seen a dragon?'

'No,' said Joey and he shot them with his bow and arrow.

Candice Garman (13)
Herons Dale (Special) School, Shoreham-by-Sea

The Curse Of The Unicorn

Long ago there lived a princess whose name was Morvena. She was very beautiful with long blonde hair and dark blue eyes. Her stepfather was a secret wizard. Morvena never knew that he was a wizard. He was horrible to her.

One day he set a curse on her. During the day she would be herself but at night she would have to rush into the forest and turn into a unicorn. If she didn't she would die.

One day her stepfather said, 'Go and pick some blackberries for a blackberry pie.'

While she was in the forest she met a handsome prince on his horse. She went back home but didn't tell her stepfather who she had met. Every day she would make up an excuse to go into the forest to see the prince. They fell in love. His name was Bercilak. Every night however she still became a unicorn.

One day her stepfather found out the truth. 'Now you will be a unicorn by day as well as by night,' he shouted at her.

Morvena didn't know that Bercilak had a curse on him as well. Every night, not recognising each other, they wandered round the forest.

Once every full moon however, so the legend says, they meet as unicorns and are very happy again.

Louise Comaschi (12)
Herons Dale (Special) School, Shoreham-by-Sea

The Princess' Necklace

This is one of the many legends about Arundel Castle.

Long ago there was a bad guy called Mark. He stole a gold necklace from the Princess Rebecca. He sold it in Spain for gold coins. Princess Rebecca's father, who was called King Edward, said, 'If I catch that man I will kill him.'

Mark came back from Spain and was very worried. He thought his best plan was to kidnap the princess. He was waiting for her behind the tree. He threw a spear at her horse and it fell down dead. She went running back to the castle and told her father the king. He rushed down to where the horse died. Mark was hiding under a bridge near the river.

The king and Mark had a sword fight which went on for half an hour. The king stabbed Mark in the arm. Mark sliced the king's leg. Mark went hobbling off but was captured later on the bridge by the king's knights. The king killed Mark. Later Rebecca sailed to Spain with her father and they went to the market where Mark sold the necklace.

She brought it back and Rebecca and her father lived happily ever after.

Becky King (14)
Herons Dale (Special) School, Shoreham-by-Sea

The Hindu Goddess

Long ago there was a statue of a Hindu goddess. She had long hair, Indian clothes and lots of arms. This is her story.

Her name was Sita named after the famous Sita. She lived in a massive palace. When she was born an Indian wizard put a spell on her that gave her lots of arms. She used her loads of arms to do everything at once. She could put her make-up on and brush her hair at the same time, stroke her cat, her dog and her horse and put her jewellery round her neck.

When she was twenty the wizard came back. She was asleep and he put another spell on her. This time he turned her into a statue but every night she came alive again and danced.

People watched her and said, 'Brilliant.' They all thought she was an amazing dancer.

Now she is a statue forever.

Ellis Ashe (14)
Herons Dale (Special) School, Shoreham-by-Sea

The Adventure Of A Dark Place

All I had over the summer holidays was storm after storm. I have dreaded that on Sunday it is going to be a nice day, so I woke up and it was sunny. How humid is that sun? Then something happened. Lightning had struck and hit me on the head and I was a bit fuzzy! You call this a story? Come on, it is a legend.

You know well about legends. I was in one. Well I had a dream about it and I fell asleep and *boom!*

I was on a treasure island. I saw pirates and treasure hanging over a tree. Then I saw arrows turning left and north and I followed them. I ended up in the sea! That was an unfortunate map. Then I saw this necklace floating on the sea. It had a skull on it and I was trying to work out what it meant.

Luckily enough I found a pirate ship that was docking. I crept on board and hid in a barrel and I could hear pirates coming. It was a cold day and I was shivering. But really I was scared. I jumped out of the barrel and there were pirates there. 'What does the symbol of the necklace mean?' I asked.

'Hi, my name is Jimmy,' said a pirate. 'The symbol is cursed and anytime you wear it and you're in the dark you have power over the world.'

Then there was a big bang and a flash. I was flying with Peter Pan! *This is amazing,* I thought, *how did I get here?*

Then Peter Pan said, 'We've got to go with the Lost Boys.'

We went in a big cave and there were loads of little boys. I said, 'Hello. Are fairies real or no - ...'

Peter Pan said, 'Don't say that, because if you do, fairies will die.'

Then I walked outside and was captured by Captain Hook! He said, 'You're coming with me boy!'

'OK, OK I'll come with you if you promise not to be evil when I'm around.'

Then I was on his pirate ship and Peter Pan came to rescue me. I was just walking the plank but Peter Pan caught me and put me on the deck.

Then there was a flash and I was in Tenerife! So at least I was somewhere nice instead of somewhere horrible. I heard this noise. It was a shark! Not any shark - it was *Jaws!* He opened his mouth and swallowed me and ... I was back home in my own bed. Thank God I am back home. I hope you enjoyed my dream.

Luke Guy (13)
Herons Dale (Special) School, Shoreham-by-Sea

The Legend Of The Killing House

Once upon a time there were two girls who went into the forest. These girls were called Lisa and Jorden.

In the forest they saw a small ruined castle. They knocked on the door. It opened by itself and there was a trap. They fell down a hole and there was a man with a knife and his name was Ben. He wanted to stick their heads on poles to add to his collection.

Because Lisa and Jorden were missing, their friends Vicky and Georgina went to find them. They found the castle too and they heard Lisa and Jorden crying.

They banged on the door and this time someone opened it. Before they got in the house Ben had the knife and killed them and stuck their heads on metal poles.

All the parents came and banged the castle door down. They got in and Ben had some of his people with him and they killed everybody.

Sometimes when it's really dark, people hear the sound of screaming in the forest ...

Jennifer Overington (12)
Herons Dale (Special) School, Shoreham-by-Sea

The Gods Of The Rainbow

Once there lived a flying unicorn and the owner brushed her every day. She was a white unicorn with a twirly horn and a soft straight yellow mane. Her name was Lilac.

The owner of the unicorn rode on Lilac every day. Every day they rode through the rainbow.

Pegasus, the winged horse, who looked a bit like Lilac without the horn, thought that Lilac might be his sister.

Pegasus looked around at Lilac and flew in circles getting all excited. He got lost and landed in Lilac's field where the unicorn was laying peacefully, relaxing. The owner saw Pegasus. She told him that he could visit Lilac once a year. That day, every year, there are two rainbows in the sky and everyone celebrates the unicorn and the horse.

But one year Pegasus got stuck in the forest. Everybody was very upset and thought that he was dead and they would never see the two rainbows again.

The owner and Lilac went to look for Pegasus, who had got scared in the forest because there were lots of animals like a Minotaur, a wolf and a dragon that was half human and horrible.

They went there and heard a moaning. Lilac rushed down to find the Minotaur looking around for Pegasus. Lilac bit the Minotaur and rescued Pegasus. They flew back for a big celebration.

You can still see the statues of them today, like gods.

Lisa Town (12)
Herons Dale (Special) School, Shoreham-by-Sea

The Magic Forest

There was a lady called Yasmin. She lived in a castle with servants. Yasmin loved living there with her jewels and a book because her dad didn't live with her. The book had pictures of her dad and Yasmin wrote her thoughts and feelings in the diary. The jewels were her dad's and they were locked up in a cabinet. She would sometimes, when she felt lonely, look at the book. Yasmin would look at the jewels and it would make her happy.

She would walk outside the castle and come to a forest with sweet little creatures like rabbits and birds that would become her friends. Yasmin loved walking with her new friends. She walked so far away from the castle, she was lost and suddenly the ugly man came out. He was walking with a stick and he had load of pus over his face. Yasmin started to cry because she was scared and lost. The old man invited her into his house.

Yasmin went into the house then a bird flew into the window and sat and sang a song. Then the old man started to turn into a handsome prince. This was unbelievable magic. Time passed and eventually they all lived in the castle and lived happy ever after.

Hazel Ellis (13)
Herons Dale (Special) School, Shoreham-by-Sea

The Thunderbird

The Thunderbird is as high as the tallest tree. He is as big as a house. His beak is curved and shines like gold. The end is sharp as a knife. His eyes are as black as coal. His feathers are bright colours in silver, gold and bronze. His feet are as strong as cement. He can fly for miles and miles. His wings are wide and strong and he can land as softly as a mouse.

When he flies at night he makes the thunder start. The wind rushes through his wings and the flashing in the sky is the lightning from the silver and golds of his feathers.

When people are walking around during the day he's hidden under the ground because he's got a special machine that opens so he can hide. The people don't know he makes the thunder.

Darren Chandler (13)
Herons Dale (Special) School, Shoreham-by-Sea

The Legend Of Dashrata

Many years ago there lived a king called Dashrata. He wasn't a friendly person. He didn't share his money. He didn't have any friends at all.

His wife had her head chopped off on his orders because her snoring kept him awake all the time and she was a lousy cook. Their children still lived in the castle but he made them into cleaners.

The castle was very rickety and falling down. It was made of cold, damp stone. It had a nice, grand fire in it and a very long dining table with all sorts of nice food like chicken, biscuits, apples, cake and other sweet food.

One day there was a battle between Dashrata and Merlin. There was lots of fire, bolts of stone, wizard fights, glitter and stars and stuff. Merlin won the battle of course.

Dashrata couldn't cope with all the atmosphere and died. Merlin turned him into stone because he didn't like the sight of him.

You can still see the statue outside the castle to this day. The expression on his face is shocked and distraught!

Lewis Pickering (16)
Herons Dale (Special) School, Shoreham-by-Sea

The Underworld

It was dark in the Underworld. Hades was being mean again. He stole the souls from the spirits that were dead and sold them to a soul-eating creature.

This creature lived in the dead river. He had jaws the size of a mammoth's head and claws as long as crocodile teeth.

In the Underworld Persephone lived there for 6 months. These had passed and Persephone asked to be free. But Hades wouldn't let her be free because he loved her too much. She said if he didn't let her go she would kill him by making a hole in the darkness, letting in the light.

When Persephone escaped, the souls flew out of the soul-eating monster and became alive again. The wounds healed and the people became immortal. They banished Hades underneath the water and he was never seen again.

Did the monster save him? Was he electrocuted and puffed into smoke by Zeus' lightning bolts? We shall never know.

Michael Empson (14)
Herons Dale (Special) School, Shoreham-by-Sea

The Killer Hampire

Jimbo was a lonely hamster. He was bored - again. So he decided to start an adventure. He nudged loose the cage door and scrambled out.

Three hours later, he'd reached the field beyond his garden. Jimbo leaped for joy and got so overexcited that he wanted to scare someone. So he put on his cape and became a hampire!

As he romped around, Jimbo noticed a fieldmouse nearby. He crept out and yelled, 'I vont to eat your cheese! Give me!' The fieldmouse jumped and sprinted off, leaving his cheese for Jimbo.

After this satisfactory breakfast, Jimbo had a nap. When he woke, he carried on his adventure. He had slept for a long while and the sun was now setting.

Suddenly, Jimbo spotted a beautiful butterfly by the stream where he was going to drink. Jimbo stepped out to ask for a date, when she screamed, *'Aaarrrggghhh!* It's a vampire! *Help!'*

At this, Jimbo was utterly insulted, 'I am *not* a *vampire!* I'm a *hampire! Goodbye!'* Jimbo marched off!

It was now dark, so Jimbo settled down for the night in the long grass.

As he awoke, Jimbo felt weird. Then he remembered where he was. Jimbo decided that he wouldn't get very far out there and he liked his cage much better. So he went home and that night, he slept more soundly than ever.

Moral 1: Never carry cheese around if there's a vicious hampire on the loose!

Moral 2: Try and try again - if that doesn't work, go home!

Amy Gilbert (12)
Highcliffe School, Christchurch

A Day In The Life Of A Door

'Oi! Door! How boring your life must be!' sneered the versatile window.

'Now you listen here! I'm fed up with you new recruits to the service. Experience is the key. Anyway, I'm a veteran. I lasted both wars. Now, seeing as you're so interested, I'll tell you about my life.'

'Shall I get my nightcap then?' sniggered the window.

'I'll start in the 1940s. Now this pub used to be a beautiful corner shop and every day children would push me open and step into a world of tranquillity and bliss, as they stood there, surrounded by all they could ever wish for.'

'Sadly though, old Mrs Deary died in the 1960s, so this shop became a barbers. Again, people would push me open and step into a world of transformation, and would walk out looking even more beautiful than before.'

'The barbers lasted for years, but in 1997 this pub was installed and customers would open me and step into a mist of confusion and, mainly, cigarette smoke. Every day, drunken brawlers are fighting and shouting. It isn't right.'

'I hate it, but there's no escape and these hinges hold firm. Oh well, enough of my yakking, the drinkers are back.'

Creeeaakkk!

'Ouch Door, have you taken your creaking hinge pills this morning?'

'No,' said the door, with a pained expression.

Will Fry (12)
Highcliffe School, Christchurch

Dream

(This is a real life story about my mum's friend's daughter, Zara, who died of tonsillitis. This is in memory of 16-year-old Zara)

Quivering waters around me, I breathe in the sweet jasmine scent, my hair stroking my neck, as I think this is the journey that is predetermined. I wish to stay here for eternity, the hours floating by, just like me, until one second, I wake up to realise that it's a dream.

I woke up with a scream! My eyes wide open with shock! I sat on the bed panting, staring around, wondering where I was, feeling drops of sweat sliding down my back. It all came back in one piercing scream. My throat hurting more than ever, Mum telling me it will be fine, while holding the phone with shaking hands and dialling the ambulance number.

They came in ten minutes and took me to the hospital, telling me that it's probably just a chest cold. I got dressed in my pyjamas and with Mum's help got into bed.

Mum sat by me talking, chatting, trying to make things OK. Then she had to go.

After going through everything, I tried to lie back and relax. I held my throat tightly, trying to stop the pain. I want to float in the river, in my dream.

Night-time. What will happen? My throat! I can hardly breathe! Panting! Groaning! Coughing! I'm dying!

I call out for the nurse! No one hears my croaky cry! I close my eyes. I stop breathing. I picture Mum in my mind, she's beautiful. She's smiling.

At my last gasp, the first strips of sunrise beam through the silent room.

Anastasia Zuyeva (11)
Highcliffe School, Christchurch

A Day In The Life Of Charlie The Cat

Inquisitive, sophisticated, intelligent and cheeky. That's me! I am a cat. Have you ever wondered when you leave for work and school, what goes on in a cat's life? Well now you can find out. Today you will follow me - Charlie the cat.

6.30am

I get up tired and hungry. My brother is already sniffing the food bowl, as usual, but there is no food! I escape the kitchen and hop up the stairs. I miaow loudly to get somebody up, to make them feed me. My brother helps. It works like a dream!

7.30am

Everybody is up now and I shoot through the cat flap into the outside world. Welcome to my playground! The morning excitement is dedicated to catching prey! Birds, frogs, mice! I spot a pigeon two times the size of me nearby. I like to challenge myself. I creep up slowly, taking careful steps. Getting nearer, nearer, *pounce!* The explosion of feathers is a delight!

12.30pm

The morning has gone so well! Suddenly, drawn by the mayhem, 'it' comes around the corner. Stupid, ugly, incompetent! Yes - a dog! It bounds towards me. Stupid 'it'! I run as fast as lightning! Much faster than the evil enemy behind. I loose him. The loser!

2.15pm

I like to keep myself in good shape, so I jump from fence to fence. Elegantly pouncing on anything in my pathway.

2.45pm

Running into the sunny room, onto my favourite chair, I snuggle down on the comfortable, bouncy cushion and dream.

Issy Donald (12)
Highcliffe School, Christchurch

The Hunting Of The Last Dragon

I was sitting down, gazing into the fire. Grandad was asleep and Mother was cooking chicken for the evening roast. My two sisters were fighting and squabbling over a wooden doll. *Click! Bang!* Father came in with a sad, lonely face and with a quivering sigh, he said, 'The village of Myers has been burnt down.'

There was silence in the house, except for the crackle of the fire. Even my sisters were as quiet as a mouse. Father's best friend had lived there. That night was dreadful for Father. There were no survivors.

On the other hand, I was getting a smacking, brand new bow and arrow from the best bowman in Dorset. I was setting out for Dorset the next day. It was only five miles away. I got up at six on the dot, took a little beer and some chicken, which I'd pinched from last night's dinner. I grabbed my money and ran out of the house and jumped onto my very best horse, Lucky and set off, galloping.

I found out that my day was not going to be my best, but my worst. When I got my magnificent bow, I headed home. The most destruction hit me first. Every house wiped out, totally. No survivors. I realised my family was gone. I was upset, angry and devastated. I cried and cried. By the time I had stopped, I could have made a puddle.

I looked up. Something was flying in the distance. By then I knew what it was, from the old tales - a dragon.

15 years later:

This dragon has killed my family and my friends. Out of ten, this is the last dragon on Earth and it's now dead. In my right hand, I have my spear, in my left, a round, Viking shield. I sneak up behind it, in its gloomy lair. I lunge my spear into its back. It goes through his heart, like a pin. It falls to the ground, like a stone. Today has been victorious.

Myles Redrup (12)
Highcliffe School, Christchurch

Voyage To Titan

(The following is an extract from Sir Jon Almond's diary, on his legendary voyage to Titan ...)

6th February, 3023

I took an absolutely exquisite spacecraft up to the 'Waterfall Space Observatory'. It was like a five-star hotel, with rockets attached. I met my crew. Their names were Phillip Smith (too talkative, but likeable anyway) and David Hughes (a chap with hypnotic contact lenses!) I'm the Captain because I'm a *'Bachelor of Deep Space Exploration'. Wow!*

7th February, 3023

After a briefing on the mission, we were ready to leave for Titan in our specially crafted ship, made of a new material - polysreneilene, by SEC (Space Exploration Corp) engineers, so it wouldn't break up at light speed. We boarded the ship, the countdown started; bracing ourselves ready for lift-off ...

8th February, 3023

Phillip's feeling sick already; at least we're saved from his banter! David wears these unusual space glasses, instead of his usual contact lenses. Our ETA, at light speed, is approximately a week or so, hopefully ...

9th February, 3023

A bizarre, unknown force has grasped our ship, pulling us through a sort of time warp; we crashed on Titan. My crew and I were out cold for a while. When I woke, I was being stared at by the strangest and most technologically advanced beings I'd ever seen. They came in droves, scuttling all over the ship, surveying it and taking electronic notes on palmtops. One 'being' barked at two others, who grunted and came over to assist it.

This was catastrophic ... they were taking over *our* ship. One stabbed me slowly, with piercing eyes. I heard Phil and Dave cry out in terror ...

Thomas Smith (12)
Highcliffe School, Christchurch

A Day In The Life Of Tinkerbell Hilton

I'm Tinkerbell Hilton. You might have seen me in the magazines. I'm the poor little runt forced into a pink sweater, way too small for me, looking like a drowned rat. No, that's Nicole you're thinking of! I'm the one whose eyes look too big for my head, used as Paris' latest accessory. No, that's still Nicole. Look, I'm the one Paris carries, OK?

So, anyway, today me, Paris and Nicole went shopping on Rodeo Drive. If you haven't heard of it, it's the best shopping boulevard in America. Anyway, the evil pair spent two hours trying to force me into tutus and superdog outfits. It's humiliating being a dog to an heiress! Then I start to pant heavily, so that the bimbo with the IQ of two, finally noticed I was tired.

She got out my bowl and a bottle of Evian water and poured it in. I tasted it - *yuck!* I could feel myself needing to be sick. So I was - all over Nicole's Jimmy Choos! Oh dear! Of course I wouldn't do that on purpose! The sad, rich girl then started to cry. How embarrassing! Paris started shouting at me, which was even more embarrassing!

'How dare you?' she was screaming.

I didn't do it on purpose! OK, maybe I did, but so what?

We all went home and I was banished to my bed. I've said it before and I'll say it again, it's tiring being Paris Hilton's pet. All you do is work, work, work and never have any play!

Jenna Lloyd (12)
Highcliffe School, Christchurch

The Adventure

The Earth was a golden gem, glistening beneath his feet. The palms were mammoth emerald hands, shielding the skylight. The path beyond was a huge achievement to accomplish.

Mariano was 12. He was confident and had one ambition. This was to complete the 'Gold Trophy'.

He edged forward, scanning for any sign of danger, turning his head like an eagle. He was abruptly faced with two paths. One looked darker than the other did, but he took the risk. He briskly strode along the winding path.

Suddenly, everything went hysterical. A trapdoor crumbled under Mariano's feet. He was hurled up and down in a trap slide, the silver sides sparkling like diamonds. He was severely bruised and his head throbbed. The dark, gloomy room looked like an impersonation of Hell.

It was dull, it was terrifying. It was neglected. Nothing stirred. Only a faint wind brushed past his face. A man entered in colourless clothes from his head to his feet. His face was as red as blood and his hair hadn't been washed for donkey's years. With slimy, gruesome bugs visible, his torso was dressed in a lime jacket, with a picture of a certain madman on it.

I was stationary. It was a slow motion battle scene. I sprinted and sprinted and sprinted, dodging like I was in a dodgeball match. I could hear his breath, right behind me. I barged down the door (I couldn't really care if I hurt myself anymore). The door, luckily, opened. I lost him! There was a golden shimmer is front of me. It was the 'Gold Trophy'. I reached out for it and ...

Adam Horwich (12)
Highcliffe School, Christchurch

A Day In The Life Of A Dragon

I woke up one cold, winter's morning, to find a knight standing in my cave's entrance. Knights are rather bad mannered and this one was no exception.

'Cor! I've found a big 'un,' shouted the knight. He ran at me with his spear, 'I'm gonna slay you!'

'Be careful with that thing, you could pole an eye out!' I replied, but he didn't listen to me. He just carried on running (he was braver than the usual knights who normally cowered behind a rock or just ran off, screaming), but I still caught him and swallowed him in one. *Mmm,* quite tasty, a little chewy and crunchy to be absolutely perfect. Obviously past his prime!

I do get quite lonely. Other than the odd knight and a few angry peasants armed with pitchforks, flaming torches and the occasional rusty axe, I don't get many visitors.

Men hunt us for our indestructible scales, which they use to make shields. They make daggers out of our razor-sharp teeth and use our heads as ornaments to hang on the walls of their rundown shacks. It's also something to do with pride, because they go down the local inn and boast about it.

I was fed up with all this and decided to take my anger out on the local village. It was market day. I acrobatically dived down and landed on a vegetable stall. I felt a bit ill after that crunchy knight, canned food never agrees with me!

The villagers screamed and ran in all different directions away from me, they're such big wimps. Some dived under stools and hid behind carts, others ran into houses and bolted their doors and windows shut. That's the trouble, you see, some are cowards, whilst some are just too big for their own boots.

I picked up a cabbage and started eating it, to wash down that knight I had devoured earlier. What can I do now? Hmm, I think I'll set fire to a woolly jumper stall. Hmm, boring! Now what? Let's try these stalls. Over they go!

After I had successfully flattened every stall in sight and up-turned a few carts just for the sake of watching some petrified people scatter like a flock of chickens, I decided I had had my fun, so I flew back home, only to find that there was a rabble of knights, rummaging around my cave. One had a scroll.

'By order of His Majesty King George II, all dragons must be executed. Right, you dragon, come here, stand still and let my knights slay you,' this bumptious knight ordered.

I let out a roar and a burst of flame, which set his scroll alight. They stood there, shaking, for a brief moment, then they fled, but not before I had let out a really impressive burst of flame, which singed a few slow coaches' cloaks.

'A little momento for you!' I shouted and with that, I settled down in my cosy cave after my busy day, and dreamt of soaring in the sky, above the clouds.

Alex Rowe (12)
Highcliffe School, Christchurch

A Day In The Life Of Daisie McDonald

'Mice, everywhere!'

I saw a beautiful land. Mice, birds and rabbits here and there. The land was so soft. A valley of string, 'Oh, I love it here. I never want to leave!' I screamed till my lungs hurt. A river of milk! I ran to the vast, milky-white snake!

'Daisie baby, come on, dinner time!'

I woke up suddenly. *Food!* I ran to the sweet-smelling tuna and dipped my teeth into the soft, white meat. A fresh dish of ice-cold water was there too.

Outside the family were playing ping-pong again. I ran to the bush, headfirst and *whoosh!* I was happy out in the great outdoors.

Molly, my greatest enemy, was walking around like she owned the place.

'All right, Daisie? Nice day today,' she said, with an evil little smile.

I looked at her and got my claws out. She did the same. I got ready to claw her face off, but she ran away before I had the chance.

I legged it back home. The family were still playing. One of the boys got out some string. He thought it was fun, so I played along. I got it stuck between my paws, kicking and jumping, I showed him who was boss.

Emily McDonald (12)
Highcliffe School, Christchurch

A Day In The Life Of Gilbert The Goldfish

Hi! I'm Gilbert the goldfish. I live in a plastic box, located at 39 Rowsbury Close. It is quite comfy in here, but the plastic is sharp and the seaweed itchy.

This morning, I was given a sharp awakening, when David, my owner, knocked me out of my tank. It was normal. He hardly cared about me. To him, I was a thing of the past. He had won me four years previously.

So, after my shaky start, I swam cautiously to the surface and collected my daily feed. Today I hoped I was going to get some lovely peace and quiet, but unfortunately, my hopes were dashed almost instantly, as I remembered it was the weekend. Weekends are hard for me. David always has a friend round.

This weekend was different though, he had invited twins, which was disastrous for me. It meant double trouble. You see, I would have to be poked, prodded and stared at. The situation worsened as I listened. I heard about behaviour problems.

After I had settled down, I saw a big hand pointing at me, so quickly, I hid behind the pump, but then I heard a creak. The lid was flung open. I shivered. A hand stretched out and grasped me by my tail. The beady eyes peered in and before I knew it, I was slithering around in the toilet sink. In came the water and in came the hands.

Suddenly, I flew into the toilet. Then they flushed it!

James Bantock (12)
Highcliffe School, Christchurch

A Day In The Life Of A Weathervane

8.30am

Here we go again! All those little brats flooding in through the gate, all revved up for another chaotic day. They're grinning and - oh God, here we go. I don't wish to look at this stupid wall. The wind down here is so rude. I used to live in London, which was much more pleasant. So much gas to turn one around, when one is facing in a funny direction and then they yanked me off the rooftop and stuffed me down here! In a school!

I miss London really. I was right on the Thames and I could see the London Eye and all around, but the worst of it is the wind down here. London is supposed to be rowdy, but here it can never decide which way to blow! It doesn't howl, it doesn't even whistle!

12.30pm

Off we go! *Urgh!* I'm going to be sick. Why can't they use spinning tops. They like to spin! Well, at least this is a better direction now. Oh, it's lunchtime. There's Tom. Here we go! *Oooo!* That was quite close, better than usual. He should get a catapult, it'd be much more effective for throwing things.

3.09pm

They're going home! Hip hip hooray! I had to face that stupid wall again. It was only for an hour though. There was a thunderstorm as well. Luckily, when I was facing outwards. Great bolts of lightning slashed the sky. Oh ... we're moving!

Hey! What's the headmaster burying? It looks like ... but it can't be ... a body!

Stephen Hutt (12)
Highcliffe School, Christchurch

Love Should Be The Last Word You Say

Sun broke. My body was full of love, as I had fulfilled my lifelong dream to get a boyfriend. I'm actually in love! The one, the only, Ken. Ken and I are going on a romantic weekend.

I slapped on some make-up, pulled on some clothes and caught the plane. We disembarked from the plane into a neat field. The fresh wind shaped my hair romantically, as I skipped up to Ken. The sun felt magnificent on my skin.

We entered our resort where toned humans were cruising around in swimwear. Ken linked his fingers between mine, as we wandered off to our hideaway.

We had a long, romantic night. Morning rose quickly and we wandered around. Our feet led us to a decrepit, ancient house. The house was a mansion and had a thick oak door, with ivy packaging the residence. We shoved the door, it creaked open. We stepped in. *Bang!* The door slammed shut. Light streamed through the ornate, coloured windows. We shivered our way forwards ...

The room was damp, like we were deep underground. Instantaneously, a white outline glided over our heads. Was it a ghost? Suddenly, a chandelier crashed to the ground and landed on Ken. Shrieks rattled through the mansion. I kissed him goodbye, as blood surrounded him ...

I sprinted to get help and as I turned to give one last look, he flew into the air, all peaceful like a spirit was holding him tight ... but all of a sudden he was flung to the ground. He was dead!

A voice cried, 'Never lie to your girlfriend about having an affair ...'

Alice Curtin (12)
Highcliffe School, Christchurch

A Day In The Life Of The Tooth Fairy

Dear Diary,

I have had the most terrible day.

It all started this morning, when my husband, Mr Toothy and I were out shopping, when the most rapid and unhesitating sky mobile went crashing into him. I was fretting all day. I'm still worried now!

What's more, when I started my shift for tooth collecting, I found that to my horror, all the money had gone! All that was left, was an open safe like a big, gaping hole in the wall. I phoned the police and said that it had gone.

I am really angry now! I found out that when children's teeth fall out, they leave rude little notes and some clever kids leave tooth-shaped bits of paper under their pillow. Really! I think I might retire! After all, no one believes in me anymore. I could live in peace, up here on cloud nine, occasionally sweeping the white marble floor or dusting the shiny silver plates. Oh well, we all have a dream. Wait, I can hear the phone ringing ...

Yes! It turns out that Mr Toothy is fine and they have found the money. I'm so relieved! My stomach was somersaulting! What's more, there was more money with my money and no one has claimed it, so now I have it! I'm so glad it turned out not to be such a bad day after all.

I'll write more tomorrow!

Heidi Barnett (12)
Highcliffe School, Christchurch

Space - Here We Come!

Yesterday, the first guests from the Milky Way Hotel (in space) landed safely at NASA. The host of the trip was Joshua Kortep. He also took Sir Alexander Ridding and Madam Mary Ridding.

The luxury Milky Way Hotel on the moon, has a space view of every planet, except Pluto. There are many facilities from a gym to a sauna, but this all comes at a hair-raising price for staying at the hotel for two weeks. Was it worth it? We asked Madam Mary Ridding and she said, 'The stay at the Milky Way Hotel was absolutely brilliant. The food was surprisingly wonderful and contained all the facilities you would expect from a five-star hotel on Earth!'

The rocket departed six weeks ago from NASA. It took two long weeks to get there and two weeks to get back, even though it travels at 120mph. This was also at an immense cost. This is what Sir Alexander Ridding said, 'It seemed to take forever and it was very claustrophobic, but the holiday was indubitably worth it in the end'.

If you wish to take this trip of a lifetime, it does come at a striking cost. Two weeks at the hotel for one person, costs £7,000 and for the trip, there and back, it costs £20,000 for one person.

Maybe slightly expensive, but now space accommodation is available!

Amy Curry (12)
Highcliffe School, Christchurch

A TV's Diary

Dear Diary,

Today has been rubbish. All the programmes were rubbish, except a few.

It all began when I was switched on at 7.30am. The parents switched me on and began watching GMTV, which was OK, but then the kids came down and switched it to the CBBC channel and watched 'Exchange', which is a totally rubbish show.

Well, after the kids went to school, I was switched to the DIY and antique programmes, which I quite enjoy, as there's some junk these people have that could be worth a fortune! It's my favourite day of the week - Friday, because there are actually decent and funny programmes on.

Well, I'll get back to you in the morning.

It was well tight, as I was watching a decent programme and then I got switched off! Luckily my mate said I could see it on his screen. Well, I'd waited for ages to watch it and I was there in a flash.

The evening came and at last, it was time for the decent programmes. First 'The Simpsons', which was a very funny episode, then the news - boring! After that, a humorous show called 'A Question of Sport', with that Scotsman, Ally McCoist. Then the music on 'Top Of The Pops'. Then it was my favourite soap, 'EastEnders'. Following that, one of the funniest comedies, Lenny Henry with Gina Ashewe.

After all that, we watched a DVD, which was pretty good. Then I got switched off and now I'm writing in my diary.

Now, I'm going to get some kip!

Neil Chapman (12)
Highcliffe School, Christchurch

Ruby

Ruby was 13, although she didn't look or act like a 13-year-old, she was one. She had ruby-red hair and very pale skin. She had been sent to a boarding school, because her parents didn't want her. She was very lonely and upset.

One day, she was walking along the corridor, everyone pushing past her, as though she were invisible, when someone punched her in the stomach, it felt like a punch anyway. She felt wheezy and dizzy and fell to the floor with a thump.

Ruby blinked a few times and then woke, 'Where am I?' she asked. 'Hello ... ? Hello ... ?' No one was there. She closed her eyes and had a dream.

She was with her mum again and they were having so much fun and laughing together. When she woke up, her mum was sitting on the bed, beside her.

'Mum?' she whispered, then she disappeared. 'Mum? Mum ... Mum?' She awoke. 'Where's my mum?' Ruby asked.

'We have some bad news,' the doctor explained, 'she was involved in a car accident ... we tried to revive her, but ...'

'But what?' Ruby weeped.

'She wouldn't come back. She's dead,' the doctor whispered.

Ruby sat crying for a while. Was this a dream or was this for real?

Amy Fowgies (12)
Highcliffe School, Christchurch

The Quest For Water

In the hot, humid, dying Egyptian desert, a young tiger cub and a mouse were playing in a drying river bed. Overhead, a hawk passed over, they called it down and it swooped down to the two animals. They asked her, 'Have you seen any water on your way here? Because we have run out.'

The bird thought and after a while said, 'Yes, I think I did, that way,' as she pointed north to a huge rock and said, 'past that rock and over the hill, you'll find a big lake.'

The three animals set off to find the lake. After a few hours had passed, they got to the rock and found a small snake slithering on top of it. They stopped and asked, 'Have you seen the water the hawk is talking about?'

'Yes, over the hill and through the forest, it's huge.'

So the hawk, tiger cub, mouse and snake set off up the hill.

After they got to the top, they saw the lake that stretched across the horizon. The snake looked up and saw lightning piercing the night-like sky and the snake turned, saying, 'I'm not going down there!' but they went ahead.

The rest of the animals carried on and as they went through the forest, a tree fell in front of them. The hawk had to carry the mouse and tiger over.

Hours passed and they reached the lake, where a turtle told them it was the sea!

Phillip Beal (12)
Highcliffe School, Christchurch

Short Story

Today, I had another flashback. Well, I think it was, but this leap was to a hundred years before! My mum says I just have a really good imagination, but I know what I saw. It was a room in a castle, that overlooked the sea, protected by tall trees.

I think that's when it happened. That's where I got my scars on my face from and on my chest, going down to my tummy. Mum says it's just a birthmark, but I know it couldn't be.

Yesterday, Mum told me I was going to a boarding school, because she wants to spend more time with her Spanish lover, Loro!

As I approached the front gate, I saw an ornate castle, with green climbers up the side windows, which had diamond shapes inside an arch. An old man came and escorted me to my room. As I walked past an unusual painting, I noticed it was covering up a door. I wondered what was behind it?

That night, I couldn't stop thinking about the painting. I was almost mesmerised.

In a daze, I set off to the secret room. Pulling back the painting and opening the door, I started to think, *where have I seen this before?*

Inside, I saw an old bed that had silk bedding. It was all covered in cobwebs. As I sat down on the bed, I had a flashback of a man. He had short black hair and he leaned over a girl with a sharp, silver knife. The man pressed the knife into her face. Blood poured out!

Suddenly, I noticed it was me! It couldn't be? I could feel the pain. I felt everything that I had felt before. I was panting hard and I couldn't breathe.

Then he got up and said, 'Now you know what it feels like to be hurt by someone you love. The same thing will happen to your granddaughter in 100 years and history will repeat itself!'

I woke up. A man was standing over me. I sunk into the bed and the darkness surrounded me.

Alexandra Calder (12)
Highcliffe School, Christchurch

Riot Breaks Out

Riot breaks out in South London on Sunday at 22.00, outside a local put. Alcoholics got kicked out of the pub, because of starting a massive fight. Blood was everywhere. People were throwing punches which felt like a rock the size of a football had hit them. The noise was horrendous. If you heard it, you would have thought you'd gone deaf.

Ten minutes after the fight began, the police finally arrived. They rushed out of their police cars and ran over to where the fight was. They tried to stop the fight, but that only made it worse. The police were struggling.

Suddenly, more police came and managed to arrest some people, but the fight wasn't over yet. The police only managed to arrest about seven people, out of 36. The riot was still big and getting bigger. The gory, gruesome, red blood was everywhere. The experience was nothing like you will every experience again.

All the people were hooligans. They were either alcoholics or drug addicts. More and more people started to join in. Then some people started lobbing glass bottles through the pub windows. Glass was smashing every five seconds.

Loads of people were injured. At the end of the fight, everyone was injured. There were about 12 serious injuries, like in a life or death situation and about 27 minor injuries.

After a long night that didn't finish until 07.00, they were all arrested and questioned and they're still being questioned to this very day.

James Edney (12)
Highcliffe School, Christchurch

Untitled

Hi! I'm Sparkle and I'm just about to go and play with my friends, Wotsit and Stripe. Wotsit is a whale and Stripe is a colourful fish! It is great living under the sea. We have races and play in the coral. 'Hey guys! Do you want to go and play ball on top of the lovely blue water?'

'Yeah! Cool!'

As the three best friends were playing on top of the water, they didn't notice a shark coming! It first started to swim around Sparkle, then it was trying to eat Stripe. Stripe swam off and the shark went after him, but Wotsit came in and scared away the shark and everyone lived! They got back to their game of ball and had a whale of a time. When they had finished playing ball, they did something else.

A few minutes later, there was a very bad storm. They went down to the bottom of the sea to get some shelter. The storm got gradually worse. It was like they were being sucked up into a whirlwind. All the fish were darting everywhere and the coral and pretty shells, were being destroyed.

The storm was worrying and I had lost sight of Stripe and Wotsit. I tried doing my famous noise, but it didn't work. After a few hours of distress, I found them. The storm had thankfully calmed down. We had got a bit hurt, but that didn't affect our friendship.

We all hope to have a few more fantastic adventures soon, so for now, goodbye from all of us!

Holly Welton (12)
Highcliffe School, Christchurch

The Story Of A Day In My Rabbit's Life

It was a nice, sunny, glorious morning and the grass looked greener than ever, even though I was in my hutch and ten metres away.

Sometime later, a boy called Jonathan said, 'Hello, Flip-flop!' and gave me some food and changed my water. I decided to chew my hutch, as I had nothing better to do.

Later on in the morning, everyone had left. I ate my breakfast and washed myself. It was very hot, so I just dozed off into a sleep. I dreamt about some long grass in beautiful meadows and playing happlily with my friends.

When I woke, it was only a matter of time before the kids were home, 'Oh please let me out, I want to run!' I said, while I was nibbling the hutch. They just ignored me and just did their normal human things for a while. Then the fun began.

I was allowed out! Yeah!

I went out into the vast garden. I felt so excited. I just didn't know which way to hop first. I kept running, but after that I was so exhausted. *Phew!* I laid down on the grass and Jonathan and Rosie stroked my back. I was in heaven!

Later I got picked up. 'I don't want to be picked up!' I shouted. I was taken into the lounge. I just ran in circles, very fast. They gave me a nice, juicy carrot and as I started to hop around the kitchen. Mum and Dad arrived home and the house was hectic.

Soon they were busy cooking supper, the phone was ringing, the doorbell was going, the TV was on and Jonathan had just gone upstairs to play his stereo. This was the final straw! It was blasting music out so loud, my ears nearly popped off! Oh, how I wished I could go back into my hutch!

I looked out of the window and the hutch door was open. All I needed to do was to get outside.

Suddenly, I was swept off my feet. Where was I going? Then I was back in my peaceful hutch. I scampered into my bed.

It was a very peaceful night and the stars sparkled brightly in the moonlit sky. The owls were hooting, the foxes were sniffing, the cat was miaowing. What a peaceful night it was!

Jonathan Swindells (12)
Highcliffe School, Christchurch

A Day In The Life Of My Dog

It was one sunny morning. I woke with a yawn and knew it would be a long day. I was moving to the beautiful countryside.

I set off early so I could get a fresh start. I was walking along my normal street lane, when my mates Dave and Bob asked if they could come with me. 'Yeah, sure,' I said happily and off we went.

Before we knew it, we were in the centre of the city. In one of the flat windows, I saw a beautiful-looking poodle. She quickly rushed down and ran up to me and asked me where I was going. I said, 'The wonderful countryside!' She then asked if she could come. 'Definitely!' I said. So, off we toddled, dodging cars screaming along the dark, black roads. We knew we weren't far from the beautiful land of wonders (the countryside).

A beam of beautiful light shone from in-between the massive, mega-monstrous buildings. 'Freedom!' shouted Perfect the poodle.

'What do you mean?' I asked.

'I have been stuck in a rotten flat all my life and have dreamed of this moment!' said Perfect.

'Well then, let's get a move on!' I said.

It wasn't long before we were out of the hideous, horrible, huge city and into the beautiful countryside. We ran as deep into the forest as we could and found a perfect spot to live and so we stayed there and lived happily ever after.

James O'Callaghan (12)
Highcliffe School, Christchurch

Short Story

'Dinner will be served for all passengers, in the main dining hall in 15 minutes time. We are heading south-east, at approximately 40 knots. We should arrive in Japan, in approximately 18 hours. We wish you a pleasant meal and hope you enjoy the rest of your journey. The time now, is a quarter to seven and don't get too drunk! Thank you. This is your Captain.' The announcement finished.

'Oh, I wonder what we are having today?' wondered Bill.

'I hope it's something nice,' replied John.

'Yeah! Same here,' said Phil, '*Mmm!* This is really beautiful.'

Screech!

'What was that?' said Phil, worriedly.

'No worries, passengers, we have only struck an underwater rock. No damage has so far been spotted, but be reassured we are checking,' announced the Captain.

'Oh, I hope there's no damage!' whimpered John.

'We're tilting - the boat's going down!' screamed Phil.

Tables were whizzing past and chairs were bouncing around the room. The boys quickly sprinted to the top of the ship and looked over the edge. The front of the boat was at least 200 foot in the air. John slipped and both Phil and Bill tried to grab hold of him, but they started to slip as well.

They were screaming for people to get out of the way. John hit someone and they flew over the edge. John grabbed onto a pole. Phil and Bill grabbed onto John for dear life. John lost his grip and all three plummeted to the bottom of the ship.

Some people were putting inflatable lifeboats into the water. Luckily, the three boys fell into the life raft too and started to float away. They disappeared across the ocean and nobody ever saw them again.

Alex Spencer (11)
Highcliffe School, Christchurch

Bracken's Big Adventure

'Please tell us!' pleaded the children. 'Oh, please tell us!'

'OK! It was when I was about your age ...' Bracken started to tell her story.

'Mummy,' Bracken whined, 'why do we have to live in this old tree?'

Bracken's mum turned to look at her. As always, her hair was a mass of red tangles and her black dress was dirty. Bracken was a fairy with a difference!

'We don't have a lot of money anyway, you don't *too* badly!'

'I know!'

Early next morning, Bracken decided she'd rule over Fairy World. She'd heard of a wand, that when you wave it, a genie appears. She also knew it was down a trapdoor at the top of a mountain.

Bracken set off. She was wearing her best black dress. She was almost at the mountains, when she heard something terrible.

'I can't wait to find a fairy! When I do, I'm going to make it grant all of my wishes!' cried a gnome. Obviously he didn't know much about fairies!

Once she had passed, Bracken flew up to the top of the mountain. She saw the trapdoor straight away. She opened it. Inside, she picked up the wand. It was so delicate and as light as a feather! She waved it and a genie appeared! Before he could speak, Bracken shouted, 'I wish I ruled Fairy World!'

Her wish was granted!

'And that's how I came to rule Fairy World!' finished Bracken.

'Wow! Tell it again!'

Bracken smiled and started to tell her story - again!

Fern Howard (12)
Highcliffe School, Christchurch

The Ants' Story

'Timber!' one of the ants shouted. Suddenly, a huge bit of mud came falling down from the raised flower bed. Everyone started to bundle around the big bit of mud and began to break it up and build an anthill, but Bob, Jack and me didn't really want to work and slowly moved into the tall grass.

We trekked for ages, but then finally came to a stop. Bob asked, 'Where are we? We keep on going round and round in circles. I think I've seen that bit of grass before.'

Suddenly, there was a huge *bang* and *thud* and a big human came stamping towards us, but luckily it didn't kill any of us.

We started to climb up a tree and saw our anthill. It was under attack from red ants. We wished we were there to help them, so we scuttled off back home, to see if we could.

By the time we got home, no one was there, but suddenly, in the grass, a survivor said, 'Help me!' before slowly dying.

If we were only there we could have helped them!

David Johnson (12)
Highcliffe School, Christchurch

The House

On a hot summer's morning, James, Joe and Arran were surfing in the chilled coastline of the south of England. They paddled in and got an ice cream, then went home to the orphanage. Arran and James did not like the orphanage, but Joe did. He liked all the cool stuff you could do with all your friends. He also loved the friendly atmosphere that surrounded him.

The next day, James and Arran were so bored, that they decided to make a run for it. Joe wasn't too sure, but he went along. They sprinted frantically out of the door, then eventually got to the abandoned house. It was falling down and derelict. Arran and James ran inside excitedly, but Joe stayed outside for a while, scarcely entering.

That night, Joe ran to the orphanage. He knocked on the door. Suddenly, a light turned on and Joe sighed with happiness. Joe entered the orphanage and felt comforted by the familiar surroundings. Joe told Maria, the owner of the orphanage, what had happened and said he would return in the morning.

The next day, the boys were hungry, so they went to the shops, but they had no money, so they stole food. Not just one or two bits, but 10 or 20 pieces each! They ran back to the house and stuffed their faces with chocolate and sweets.

That night, Joe returned to the orphanage to sleep, but when he returned to the house the next morning, there was no trace of Arran or James, but there were bloodstains down the staircase, as though someone was dragged down.

Arran and James have never been seen since that day and Joe has never left the orphanage again!

James Gutsell (12)
Highcliffe School, Christchurch

Buddy - The Puppy Diary

Dear Diary,

These two days have been a bit of an adventure. It all started when my mum decided to take us on a walk, but it wasn't a walk at all! We went into town and it was busy. We started to get trod on and anyway, my sister, Whisper and me, couldn't keep up.

It was 10pm at night and we were hungry. There was a very colourful supermarket, so we decided to step inside. We came to the section of dog food and so my mother decided to start climbing to get us a tin of food, but we got caught and we got kicked out, so we ended up still with hungry tummies.

We walked coldly down the busy street, until we came to a huge house. Outside was a big red dish full of food, so we started eating and then carried on walking.

We came to a forest and started walking in to it. My mum came across a hole, so we started to look in it, but all of a sudden, my mother noticed that baby Flossy had gone. We were so tired though, that we just fell asleep.

The next morning, my other brother found that I had gone. 'Mum, Buddy's gone and got herself lost,' said Joe.

I had only gone off for a walk and came across an owl called Hoot. We played a game called 'Find the Leaf', when all of a sudden, a storm came and the rain started to fall down. I started to get frightened and worried. I didn't know where or which way to go. I was shivering, but I found a very kind rabbit who led me to warmth and shelter.

Her name was Floppy and she was the mother of four. Their names were Peter, Missy, Carrot and Dol. They were all very sweet and well-behaved. I told them in my own language who I was, but they didn't understand, so I just sat there, thinking of my family and how they were scared of the thunder.

I started to walk out and to find my way back, but I couldn't, it was far too dark and cold. I was shivering, but I didn't care. I started to walk carefully, looking for my mother and at last I came across them. I was safe! I was fine! My mother licked me with joy, but still I had to find my baby sister, Flossy, so we started to go the way home.

We found her, at home, safe!

That was my adventure!

Carolyn Franklin (12)
Highcliffe School, Christchurch

A Day In The Life Of The Sun

I make everyone happy, because I'm the sun.

'I'm the sun, I'm yellow and I come out in the day and go away at night!' I exclaimed.

One day, I went to make the place lovely and sunny so everyone could enjoy the weather on the beach. The most stupid, disgusting, awful, selfish, fat, horrible, plump lump decided to ruin it! The rain cloud! That's who it is, the rain cloud. I hate him! He is the worst rain cloud in the whole of the entire Earth! Well, I think that's enough said about him!

Anyway, getting back to what happened. As I was saying, he ruined the lovely day for me, because he had to push me out of the way and rain on the one lovely day I was going to make. How rude!

The next day, I went in and I let the rain cloud go out and ruin the day, but it was OK, because I did what he had done to me. So, the rain cloud goes out and then I run back and forth, in and out, of the rain and I did it lots of time to annoy him and guess what? He got really angry with me and I just laughed my big, yellow head off!

Suddenly, he came bursting out and started to rain whilst I was still out. I thought to myself, *I've got to win*, so I persevered and he gave up and I was so happy!

I shone my golden heart off the rest of the day!

Lauren Coulson
Highcliffe School, Christchurch

Untitled

It was Sunday morning and like normal, everyone was up. I had my breakfast, then the phone rang. It was my dad, so I gave the phone to Mum. I went into the living room, with Lucky, our dog. He was barking because of the phone. Then I heard, 'Take that dog for a walk, please.' That was Mum. She always asks me to take the dog for a walk. Sometimes I get fed up with it, but this time I didn't mind.

I got the lead and went with Lucky. Lucky jumped out of the front door and I didn't realise that the gate was open and Lucky jumped out. All of a sudden, I heard a screech of a car and I ran out to get Lucky. The next thing I knew, I was in hospital.

People say I am in a coma and they're trying everything to try and get me out of it.

I am lying here alone right now and I can hear the door opening. I think it's Mum and Dad. They're talking to me.

'Please wake up! You were in a car accident. You remember Robbie, when you went to take Lucky for a walk? Well, sadly, Lucky died.'

It all went silent for a few minutes. I am upset. I am upset not just because Lucky died, but because when you're in a coma, you can't show any emotion, say anything or move anything. You know you're alive, but you just can't tell them.

I have been in hospital for six months now and I can hear people whispering. What if they're going to cut my life support off? I'm scared, very scared.

Lucinda Coulson
Highcliffe School, Christchurch

A Day In The Life Of A Foal

I opened my eyes after a nap. I looked around and saw my mother staring at me. Then I looked towards the old, wooden door. Looking under the door were my friends, the puppy with a pink nose, a duckling with big feet and a calf with odd spots. I was spotty and my mother was not. It was a bit strange, but I was used to it.

My mum helped me to get up. I asked her why I was spotty, like I always did and she said, 'Because you're special!' like she always did. My name is Pebble.

I went exploring again with my friends, the puppy, the duckling and the calf. They all said that I could play with them today and that they had something to show me. So I followed them. They led me to millions of horses and I asked every single one of them, if they knew why I was spotty. They said they didn't know.

I was very upset and was playing in the forest. On the other side of the opening, was a spotty filly, galloping along. I asked her why we were spotty. She laughed and said it was our breed and that we were special to be spotty. I asked her if she wanted to spend the day with me, so she did.

I met her mum, she met mine and they talked for an hour while we played in the wood.

That was the best day of my life, because that's the day I fell in love!

Joanna Bennet (12)
Highcliffe School, Christchurch

Nobody Saw It Coming

Nobody saw it coming, but things like this always seem to happy when nobody expects it. Occasionally, one hears the distant wail of sirens from his kitchen, living room or bedroom and only the most deeply concerned wonder, who's involved tonight? A burglar? A building on fire? A child in agony? Your mind will start racing - teeming with questions - when a roaring cascade of red and blue, stops nearby.

Tony was not unfit. In fact, many would happily admit that he was the most active person around. He was respectable, rich and in his late sixties. Looking at it this way, what was about to happen had always been inevitable.

Donning his pastel tracksuit, Tony jogged, at a surprisingly rapid pace, to his newsagent's, just like every other morning. This was just before it happened.

Nobody heard him go.

Vic knew what he had to do. Three-hundred thousand the guy had said, but Vic had never wanted to do it. He just needed the money.

Waiting outside the manor house with a silenced gun and a considerably heavier wallet, Vic was anxious to get it over with, but Tony saw Vic, before Vic saw Tony.

There were two ambulances, a police car, a corpse and a missing person.

Everybody knew what had happened, because Tony was never seen again.

Cal Russell-Thompson (13)
Lake Middle School, Isle of Wight

Destiny

She'd always known it. She was looking for something. She just wasn't sure what it was. Trinity reached up a hand and tentatively poked her tingling scar. As usual, darkness began to cloud her vision and Trinity wondered where she would end up this time.

When she awoke, she straightened her supple profile, realising with no surprise, her unfamiliar surroundings. A man was perched on a marble stool just as ancient as himself. He leant closer to Trinity, eyes opening to reveal ... emptiness? No, everything, if she gazed deeply enough!

The antique man spoke slowly, as if trying to remember how, 'You know what you must do. It is your fate, your destiny.'

'I don't believe in either!' quipped Trinity, her voice as arched as one slender, dark eyebrow.

'Perhaps not,' replied the man, no trace of emotion in his hollow voice, 'but if I'm wrong, if neither destiny nor fate exist, why are you here?'

Feeling ashamed, Trinity realised that he was right and felt an overwhelming compulsion to look down at her chunky black boots. 'Where do I sign?' she asked, cheekily, almost managing to look sincere. Her toughness had returned.

The old man looked disapprovingly, before stepping away from her, 'Just do as you did before.'

In a flash of white, they were gone. He would never set foot on Earth again. She would save another, who would salvage another ...

Eventually, the human race would be safe from itself. Its own anger, greed and jealousy.

Alexandra Kingswell (13)
Lake Middle School, Isle of Wight

The Fire

The fire blazed its inside a fiery-red with ferocious velocity. It engulfed the house with such force, that the weak-timbered little building could not withstand it. Like a servant bowing to its master, the building collapsed with a cascade of timbers. As it smashed to the ground, a shockwave hit the surrounding houses, forcing the villagers from their slumber, into the harshness of day.

Even though the building was collapsed, it continued to burn. It burned for a long time and many people stood there, watching. It was as if it could not be stopped. Yet, as the fire service arrived and the froth of awaiting water was thrown on the fire, it gently cooled and was eventually brought under control.

Searchers observed the smouldering rubble with dismay, looking not for survivors, but bodies. When nothing was found so far, they let out a sigh of relief.

However, there in the corner, was a body. It was hacked at in places and heavily burnt. Silence.

The silence was broken by the wail of a baby. It shattered into a thousand pieces and each shard was embedded into the rescuers souls and hearts.

Verity Goodyear (13)
Lake Middle School, Isle of Wight

Untitled

'We're almost there, Lucy,' Mum shouted to me from the front seat of the car. 'Are you listening?' Mum asked, while stopping the car in a lay-by to rest. I could see that she was exhausted from driving all day, so I opened the car door and followed her onto the grassy verge nearby.

A moment later, a picnic cloth was strewn across the ground, with a small, delicious feast in the centre. 'Wow, Mum, this looks amazing!' I exclaimed, at the sight of the food. Mother and I ate the food and then got back into the car and went to sleep.

The first stone hit the car windscreen at midnight. I woke up and staring into the blackness of the woods, wondered what had happened. I woke my mother, 'Mum, Mum, wake up,' I whispered, 'I think there's someone out there.'

'Don't be silly,' Mum reassured me, 'who would be out here in the middle of the motorway?'

'Them!' I answered, quivering like a mouse that knows it's being watched by a cat.

'Lucy!' Mum shrieked. 'Get underneath the back seat! *Now!'*

Emerging from the shadows of the trees, was a gang of 70 men in balaclavas. Trying to ignore the useless screams of my mother, being dragged off, by her hair, into the darkness of the forest, I reached into the glove compartment and there was the mobile phone.

I dialled 999 … the line was dead!

Katie Woodhouse (13)
Lake Middle School, Isle of Wight

The Unusual Adventure Of Bob The Milkman

It was 9.30am and I was out delivering milk as I always do. (I'm Bob, by the way.)

Suddenly, there was a gunshot and a, *'Nooooo!'*

The commotion had come from Ernest's house. I put the pedal to the metal and sped down the road at two miles an hour in my milk float. I ran inside and found Ernest, holding a pack of Werther's Original, on the floor, dead. I reached down and took one of the sweets. 'Just as I thought,' I said, 'toffee!' I also found a gun, the murder weapon, and a set of false teeth. I decided to solve the mystery ...

I went to see Gertrude, Ernest's widow. She told me of an argument between herself and Ernest. 'I could have killed him!' she said.

'You did kill him, didn't you? You told me that the argument was about false teeth. I found a set at the crime scene,' I said.

Gertrude looked shocked.

I continued, 'You shot Ernest and took the teeth!'

'Alright, I killed him! Those were my teeth!' Gertrude screamed.

I took out my phone and punched in 999.

A month later Gertrude was in jail and I had been knighted for 'Services to Milkmanning'!

I returned to my job, ever vigilante, in case another murder happens. If so, Sir Bob will leap into action, as fast as my milk float will carry me!

Chris Browning (13)
Lake Middle School, Isle of Wight

Andy The Ant

Andy the Ant was a black ant. He was the same as any other ant, except that he was very forgetful. His usual job was to move the dirt away, to make a nest. The only problem was, one day Andy forgot his way and walked off in completely the wrong direction.

He walked for miles, trying to find the nest, but he couldn't find it. Eventually, Andy managed to find a busy town. Any town was dangerous for an ant, but Andy decided to investigate.

Suddenly, he came to a garage. Andy didn't know what on Earth this was, so he went in, just avoiding the sliding door.

After a quick look around inside, Andy decided to find an ant town. Luckily for him, on the opposite side of the road, was a sign saying, 'Ant Casino'. Being very nosy, he decided to go in. A short time later, Andy was drinking slug juice and having a great time. He could afford to buy the juice, because he had placed a bet with all his money. Fortunately, he had won, one million drops.

As Andy was leaving the club, female ants started to follow him ... Unfortunately, Andy forgot what a road was and stepped out, not noticing a road sweeper, sweeping the road. The bristles of the brush started to spin Andy around so fast, that he couldn't stand the force. Andy died while spinning around. We no longer know where Andy is.

Andrew Brailsford (12)
Lake Middle School, Isle of Wight

A Day In The Life Of Charles

Friday 20th August 2016

As the number of deaths slowly reached the big ten, I felt as though a part of me died with my victims. Well, it's not as if I meant to kill nine of them, but you know the guys who are so full of themselves, that you just want to sink your nails into the necks and hope they're not there tomorrow? They were like that, but the tenth was a little different.

The day started off like any other day. I got up, had a wash, had a spot of breakfast, then one of *them* entered the room. I could smell his fear, as I turned around and looked him straight in the eye ... and then, I asked him to let me out of the house. It was Jack.

With the LA summer sun beaming down, like a gas-lit flame, I felt my legs getting weak, as I thought, *it's time for lunch,* so I stopped off at my usual alleyway, behind Jo's Pizza Palace and tried to find any leftover food. I was in luck. Half an anchovy and cheese pizza was laying in a box, on the bin.

Once I'd finished it, my stomach roared at me, as if to say, 'Is that all? I'm still empty!'

So I looked around and saw it ... my next victim. I pounced ... then sunk my claws into its heart, I ripped him open and ate the tasty insides of the defenceless mouse.

Being a cat, I can get away with murder!

Steph Hewitt (13)
Lake Middle School, Isle of Wight

Weekly London

Londoners had the shock of their lives this week, when a group of pink and purple elephants paraded down Regent Street! The elephants were seen at around 5.50pm on Saturday night!

A group of teenagers were shocked to see the elephants.

'We were well surprised! Elephants? Walking down Regent Street, in London!' 13-year-old Mya Williams told us.

London zookeepers couldn't even explain the strange happenings and quickly and efficiently, the pink and purple elephants were transported back to the local zoo, London Zoo, to be cleaned up and fed.

The pink and purple colours, were said to be paint that had landed on the elephants whilst a building was being painted, but this still wouldn't explain where the elephants came from. London Zoo had all 32 of their elephants counted and caged during the emergency, so where did these creatures appear from and what were they doing in London?

Well, animal expert Jillian Millhurst gave us an exclusive interview:

'These elephants, as strange as it sounds, must have been living in the city, or at least being kept by someone! To be able to keep elephants without anyone noticing, is quite a hard task! Somehow, these elephants were walking freely, without a care in the world!'

Alice Bradley (13)
Lake Middle School, Isle of Wight

Gerald The Mouse And The Holy Cheese

Gerald the mouse lives behind the skirting board in the loft of the Strong household.

One day, Gerald decided to go all the way down the stairs of the loft and to the kitchen, where in the fridge, is the Holy Cheese! He is an adventurous mouse and has attempted this journey many times before, but had failed miserably, because of the dreaded cat, Pete! This time, Gerald was finally ready.

So, Gerald set off by climbing down the loft stairs and then made his way to the lounge. There, he scanned the calendar for the day. He quickly read through the Strong family's plans. Pete went to the vet at 12.30 - great! Exterminator due 3.00 - what *exterminator?* The Strongs must have found out about Gerald. Gerald had to change his plan; he had to be out of the house, with the Holy Cheese, before 3pm.

He looked at Simon the Budgie, in his cage.

'Morning Gerald, what are you doing?' squawked Simon.

'I'm off to get the Holy Cheese,' replied Gerald.

'Good luck! Take the thread next to my cage, if you want,' offered Simon.

'Thanks,' said Gerald and set off with the cotton reel, which was very awkward to carry.

In the kitchen, he climbed up the larger drawer handles. On top, he found a paper clip and fixed it to one end of the thread. He took aim and threw it towards the door of the fridge. It flew through the air and with a lot of luck and not much skill, it fastened around the handle and wedged fast. Next, he pulled as hard as he could and the door opened. He swung along the thread, jumped off and landed next to the Holy Cheese! Gerald felt a warm, glowing feeling, as he went to touch it. He scoffed some of it and then put the rest in his bag. He glanced at the clock - it was 2.55pm. He had to hurry.

He jumped down and made for the front door. He climbed up onto a table and stepped onto the doorknob. He pushed on the letter box and hopped out. He flew through the air and landed on the doormat. Gerald scurried off and hid behind the picket fence. He then waited, breathing heavily.

Within what seemed like seconds, the exterminator arrived and went indoors. Gerald breathed a sigh of relief and scampered off down the pavement to find a new home!

Harry Fisher (12)
Lake Middle School, Isle of Wight

A Day In The Life Of A Baby

My throat is so dry, I've been screaming for so long. When is someone coming to get me?

I hate having a dirty nappy and that's what I've got right now! When I was just about to give up hope of ever getting my soiled nappy changed, a woman I see every day, came in, slightly tired and changed my nappy at long last.

When I had stopped crying at how long she had taken getting to me, she lifted me out of my cot and put me in a high chair in the kitchen. She was opening her mouth as if to speak, but I couldn't understand her. She then opened a jar and shoved some food down my throat! It was absolutely dire!

Once she had stopped torturing me by feeding me that disgusting food, she sat me down on the living room floor, opened her mouth again and gave me some toys to play with, while she made some food for herself. While I was playing, a tall man came into the room and picked me up. I screamed with delight.

The woman said something to the man, picked me up and took me upstairs to get dressed. She put my favourite outfit on, my Winnie the Pooh outfit. It had all different colours all over it, that's why I like it so much.

I was beginning to feel sleepy. I closed my eyes, not knowing that the next time I opened them, I would talk!

Adele Beston (12)
Lake Middle School, Isle of Wight

Migration

The great herbivores of Africa, began their journey, knowing the troubles that would face them; some killed by starvation or lack of water, other taken by predators. However, most of them would make it.

As they neared the main river, a silent, moving shadow swam towards them. The crocodile quickly chose his target: a wildebeest calf, only a week or two old. The huge reptile suddenly lunged out of the water and grabbed the calf's muzzle in his mouth. He soon drowned the calf and began to eat. The grazers crossed the river soon after, knowing that for them, it was safe.

A while later, when the animals were grazing, a pride of lions were stalking them. Even the male of the pride had come; it would be a big kill. The lions stalked the zebra, having already chosen their next meal. They waited until they were within five feet of the zebra, to leap onto its back and the male throttled it, by clasping his mouth around its throat.

After these things happened many times, the herbivores finally came to the Mara River, the final obstacle of their journey. Predators of all kinds were here. The big cats, the dogs and the crocodiles. Spread out, they all prepared to hunt, their cubs hiding away, protected from heavy hooves and sharp horns.

Wildebeest, zebra and many of the other grazers, all species suffered losses, but the huge numbers were hardly affected, so the journey of migration never ends.

Cara Hetherington (12)
Lake Middle School, Isle of Wight

Jim The Monkey

Swinging from tree to tree, eating golden bananas and even snoozing in the open trees! That was part of every monkey's life, however, it had been part of Jim's life, until *now!*

With Jim's furry coat of skin and his long, soft tail rapping itself around branches, it was quite hard to think that anything would change in his life. He had lived his life normally, until today and that's when it happened.

Happily, the small monkey swung through the overgrown rainforest with his tail trailing. Suddenly, he felt his tail slide against a smooth surface. Jim turned around and, to his amusement, found a gleaming surfboard in front of his bright eyes.

Instinctively, he picked up the gleaming surfboard with his tail, and swinging from tree to tree, until he eventually arrived at the tropical beach, with golden sands and a shimmering sea.

Jim placed the surfboard onto the sparkling sea and carefully, he lifted one of his hind legs up and situated it on top of the surfboard; he then raised his other leg and did the same thing as before!

As the board drifted out into the tropical sea, so did Jim. He stood upright on the board, beginning to balance and manoeuvre himself around the sea. The board picked up speed. The closer Jim got to land, the sooner he could picture an image on the beach. It was a surfing competition!

Jim decided to join in. He competed but didn't win, but he really enjoyed the experience!

Richard Holt (12)
Lake Middle School, Isle of Wight

Live8 Rocks The World

Yesterday, Live8 rocked the world, with concerts staged at worldwide venues, bringing awareness to the Make Poverty History campaign.

Live8 is being used to highlight the plight of the African people, which will be discussed at the G8 Summit in Gleneagles.

Millions of people watched the concerts around the world and billions tuned in to watch via television and radio.

Many great singers, like Sir Elton John, Duran Duran, McFly and U2, turned out in countries all over the world to perform.

In Hyde Park, where 200,000 people watched the performance, Robbie Williams was the star of the show, with some amazing songs and audience participation.

Bob Geldof addressed the public in London, urging people to march to Edinburgh to lobby the G8 summit; he also couldn't resist singing!

In South Africa, Nelson Mandela said how wiping out poverty is an act of justice.

The message of Live8 was simple, the G8 should wipe out the African debt and provide aid packages for them to start on the trail of making poverty history. It looks as though it might happen now, 20 years after the original Live Aid concerts. We will all wait with anticipation to see the results of the G8 Summit next week.

Jamie Collings (13)
Lake Middle School, Isle of Wight

A Day In The Life Of A Tortoise

I slowly woke up and opened my eyes. It looked like it was going to be a hot day, so I slowly moved in the direction of my food tray to see if I had any food. Luckily, there was some, placed on my small tray. There were two sliced tomatoes, some cucumber and a lettuce leaf. I ate the lettuce and hurried off to see if my friend Toad was around. He's usually by the pond, but he wasn't there today. Maybe he is ill? I went, then.

Oh no! It's the dog from next door, chasing me! I'm going as fast as I can. He always tries to get me, so I stop and tuck my body inside my shell. There, he can't see me anymore! *Phew!* He's gone! I don't know why he doesn't like me, it's not like he can really eat me! At least he's gone.

I think I will have a sleep. Crawling away from a dog really takes it out of you. *Aahh!* That's better! A nice nap always makes me happier.

Now for some tomatoes. *Wow!* They taste really good!

I'm going to look for Toad now. He's still not there. Never mind!

The sun is setting now, so I am going to go to sleep. Hopefully, Toad will be around tomorrow!

Ruth Chambers (13)
Lake Middle School, Isle of Wight

Don't Let Me Go In There!

Oh no! I know what this is all about and I'm not going in there, not after the last time.

Can't you tell I'm unhappy, by the way that my tail's all fluffed up and my claws are out? Oh please, I'm really sorry about eating the hamster and I promise I'll be good! *Aarrrggghhh!*

What have I done to deserve this? It's that place again, isn't it? I can tell by that horrible wet dog smell. Hold on! I think I've just spotted myself a tasty, juicy, gerbil snack. Maybe if I miaow loud enough, they'll let me out of this grubby basket.

What? What do you mean shut up? Well I never! Snowbell? What do you mean? Who said my name? No, no, please don't let me go in there! *Aarrrggghhh!*

Huh? I have not lost weight, I'm as fit as a fiddle! Thank you, but there is nothing wrong with my hearing!

Ha, ha! See! I told you there was nothing wrong with me. Now come here and give me a rub behind the ear!

Purrrrrrrrrr!

Sammy Cowling (13)
Lake Middle School, Isle of Wight

Untitled

I really thought they loved me. I really did! I arrived as a Christmas present for the little girl. She smiled and cuddled me and looked after me. Her friends came round and she showed me off. Her friends treated me like a very special toy that they had always wanted.

The big man was threatening. He didn't feed me or look after me. I'd go and sit with him, but he'd push me away. I would lay by the door until the little girl came home from school. Then I was happy again.

Eventually, the little girl got bigger. Some things stopped; she didn't play with me much; she hardly trained me; she shut the door and I couldn't get in. I would cry by the door, but it was hardly ever opened. I no longer got treats and I was frightened that she didn't approve of me. I would sit and roll over and show her I wanted her to be my friend again ...

The big man turned up at home walking very strangely. I got small glimpses of him hitting the little girl. That's why she was never with me!

One day, I tried to save her. I bit the man's leg until he screamed, but then he hit me hard around the nose, over and over. Then, he put me outside. A dustbin fell on me, leaving crimson marks on the floor.

The food in the bin was bad and my yellow fur was dirty. The door never opened again.

Becky Watson (13)
Lake Middle School, Isle of Wight

The Light Traveller

The sea was rough; it spat spray all over the pale white cliffs of the Isle of Wight. Yet, in the distance, a light appeared. It was blue and shimmered occasionally like an extremely bad oil lamp.

Eventually, the light became opaque, splashing a green beam like a searchlight across the water.

Where the light had been, a figure now stood. He was broad-shouldered and appeared to be taller than any other man. His face was different, vaguely human in appearance, but didn't explain the neatly cut scars that tracked across his face, crude disfigurements that ran directly down his features.

The man altered his hat, as it had become askew with travelling through the blue light.

The traveller slowly reached inside the left sleeve of his neatly pressed dinner jacket and withdrew a slender metal spike. He looked about him, before plunging the spike into the ground. As he dug the sharp point into the sand and rock, the end began to shimmer; it glowed a fluorescent orange. Next the man once again reached into his jacket and this time pulled out a watch. He looked carefully at the hands and then, as he put the watch back, twisted the end of the spike.

A blue light flashed; it modelled the form of a wall, before changing into a rusty wrought iron gate. The gate swung open as if an invisible servant had opened it. The man walked through the gate and as he left, he tossed a scrap of paper to the ground. It read: 'We shall meet again'.

Lewis Clark (12)
Lake Middle School, Isle of Wight

The Giant Squid

Sailing across the Pacific to invade Japan, in order to receive America's dignity, along with their ruler, who was unfortunately kidnapped. Something scared the Americans, lurking beneath the sea ... it was a myth that a giant creature lived under the Pacific Ocean, some say it was an octopus and some said a sea-human, or a giant squid.

As the sailors crossed the ocean, the waves became taller and more powerful, but there was no wind force whatsoever.

'Strange,' said the first sailor.

'Very,' said the second.

On the fourth day, one member of the NAN (National American Navy) was found hanging from the mast, dead. This lurking creature, seemed to have left a tentacle behind.

'This is no sea-human, nor an octopus. It must belong to a giant squid,' declared the captain.

On the fifth day however, the sea was extremely rough and growing more so by the hour.

Suddenly, a long, slimy tentacle started to suffocate the ship, squeezing its decks. The men on board were running for their lives, heading towards the storage facility, where there were spears and harpoons. They sprinted carefully, getting into their positions to kill this giant beast. The squid had now killed two more sailors and only two remained. A fog siren echoed, suddenly.

'It is the NAN, they've come to *saaaaavvvvvveeeeee* us.'

Sailor four was quickly attached with the squid's tentacle. The squid had now covered the whole of the ship with his tentacles, wrapping the ship in its grasp ...

Bradley Crees (12)
Lake Middle School, Isle of Wight

A Day In The Life Of A Mouse

It was a normal day in the house. I was asleep while everyone got us, dressed and made their way outside to get a tan and to sit outside in the beautiful, warm sun and to play, while the weather was still lovely from the passing heatwave.

Meanwhile, I would be waking up, getting into my clothes and walking out of my 'den' to go and find my breakfast for the morning. The fridge would normally be packed, but with the food having to feed the whole family, like today, the fridge would be nearly empty, so I started to look.

Butter, pork pie (yuck!) and cheese ... that will do, so I ate the piece of cheese. It's my favourite, so I was all right. Now it was time for trouble ...

I never really liked cats much, but the majority of the family did, so we got Bob, the pesky little cat, so I make as much trouble as I can and I can normally hide before anyone finds out it's me winding the cat up. That's the best part of the summer - the whole day to wind the cat up. Terrific!

Then I lounge around the empty, silent house. I can relax without a care in the world and no more cats to worry about. I love my life, lounging around. No hurry, no electric and heating bills to pay.

So, have you guessed what or who I am yet? OK, I'll tell you ...

I'm a mouse!

Kali Farmer (13)
Lake Middle School, Isle of Wight

A Day In The Life Of A Fish

I've always wondered what it is like to be a fish, whether in a tank or the deep blue sea. So today, I am going to live as a fish and, when I come back, write exactly what it is that fish do in an average day, then I will always remember, oh! and become famous and rich!

I used to wonder if it would be like the poem I once read. It said things like: eat, swim, play, goodnight! That sort of thing, but with more to read. It sort of repeated itself, so it was cheating really, I suppose, but people didn't realise.

Anyway, I must explain that to live the life of a fish, I have created an invention. I call it The Evolutionator, which will turn me into a fish and then, after twelve hours, it will automatically turn me back into a human, so that I can finish this story as a fish with a three-second memory and remember forever. So, here I go ...

Now I have lived for a day as a fish, I have come back to write this as a story, and here it is ...

Sorry, I've forgotten! Well, what do you expect me to remember, having the three-second memory of a fish?

So, still I wonder, what it's like to be a fish. I don't think I will ever know what it's like, never ever, ever.

Umm? What was I saying again?

Amber Trueman (12)
Lake Middle School, Isle of Wight

First Day Nightmare!

Lucy McGowan and her best friend, Rachel Lawson, were just starting secondary school. They had had a fantastic seven years at Redbridge School, but didn't have any idea about what to expect! Rodious School was very different! People went missing, mysterious deaths occurred and anyone who goes there, never leaves! Unfortunately for them, Lucy and Rachel had no idea!

They walked through the hallway and screams echoed. The girls looked around, but kept walking. They started up the stairs. Rachel was at the top, waiting for Lucy, when the stairs disappeared and Lucy began to fall.

Rachel grabbed her hand. 'This school ain't normal!' she shouted.

'You think?' Lucy replied, hanging on for dear life.

Rachel tugged Lucy up and she collapsed on the floor, breathing heavily. The stairs reappeared and when Rachel looked at the window, it was bricked up.

Suddenly, time went very fast! The students started moving fast, but the two girls were normal.

'It's not just the school,' Lucy said, taking a look around, 'it's them too!'

They ran downstairs, towards the door, which also sealed itself up! The girls started thinking about what they could do ... and suddenly, it came to Lucy.

'We should just wait ... trust me!'

The two girls sat by the school doors and then, 20 minutes later, they opened and a man walked in. They leapt outside, so the doors couldn't close on them. They were out!

'We did it!' Rachel told Lucy. 'We survived secondary school!'

Stephanie Button (12)
Le Rocquier School, Jersey

A Short Story

Marie lived with her mum, dad and her dog, Spotty. All her life, Marie had lived in Gooseberry Cottage on the top of Hallway Hill, but one day, Marie's mum got a new job in town, so they had to move to Palace House on Golden Street. Although the street and the house sounded clean and posh, they were exactly the opposite.

Marie had a hard time settling in, especially at school, but when her dog Spotty went missing, Marie didn't think her life could get any worse.

When Spotty went missing, Marie searched high and low, but she still couldn't find him. 'Spotty, where are you?' she yelled at the top of her voice. Then Marie saw the window was open in the living room and so she ran to the window and jumped straight out. It was pouring with rain and Marie was now soaking wet.

Suddenly, Marie heard a very loud noise coming from the garage. She rushed over, to find a big pile of boxes and junk all over the floor. When she found Spotty lying under the pile, she jumped up feeling very pleased, but also worried in case Spotty was hurt.

The next day Marie and her mum took Spotty to the vet's and the vet said that he was fine and that he had just broken his leg.

Kimberley Hamon (12)
Le Rocquier School, Jersey

Myth Legend

The fire-breathing dragon soared high above the mighty volcanoes, in search of a new nest. The dragon had been flying around for hours, but then he saw the perfect spot.

When he'd built his nest, he wasn't pleased with it, because of the annoying dragon that was circling the nest. It was a blue, scaly dragon and the red dragon thought, *can't I have any privacy?*

The blue dragon was now flying even lower and closer to the nest and blowing leaves over it. The red dragon got up and took a deep breath and blew a big fireball right at the blue dragon. The blue dragon fell to the floor.

A couple of minutes later, he came back up and whipped his tail right at the red dragon. The red dragon then headbutted the blue dragon and clawed him. He fell to the floor with an almighty crash.

Jack Neville (12)
Le Rocquier School, Jersey

Night Stalker

One night, when the moon was full, something ventured out of the woods. It was a beast of the night, a werewolf and it was hungry for flesh. It had been waiting for three days for someone to come into the woods, but no one had come.

It found itself a city, a big city with plenty of meals, but it had to lay low.

In this city there was a hunter, a werewolf hunter, with every sort of weapon imaginable. He had silver bullets, silver swords and knives and even silver nets. He was the hunter and the werewolf was his prey.

So he went hunting, hunting for the werewolf. He looked everywhere in the city, until he found a trail of blood in the underground train station, where a train would have been and stopped.

Suddenly, the silence was shattered by the sound of a train. As it stopped, he saw that the windows were red and the lights had gone out. As he entered the train, it started moving and the hunter nearly fell over.

From behind him came a roar, 'Where are you?'

He grabbed his sword and swung it around, cutting up chairs, but no werewolf. He left the train and the last thing he saw, was five werewolves standing over him.

Branden Delahaye (12)
Le Rocquier School, Jersey

A Day In The Life Of My Mum

I have to go to work. I have just fed the baby and have to drop it off at the childminder's house.

I'm now driving to work, but I have to drop my younger daughter at school. My older daughter goes to the same secondary school that I work at.

I have arrived at school and now I'm going to look at my worksheet to see what I'll be doing today.

My first lesson is to go and help some Year 10s in English and I'm helping them with their short stories.

The bell goes and I have to go to maths with the Year 9s. In this class they were adding and subtracting.

The bell goes again and it's lunchtime one. I go and eat from a bag of food that I have brought from home.

The bell goes again and now I'm doing geography and the Year 7s are doing maps. It's a double lesson.

The bell goes again and now it's lunchtime two. I go and get something from the canteen.

The bell goes again and now I'm off to do art with the Year 8s.

The bell goes at ten past three and school is finished. I wait for my older daughter to come out of school and then go and pick up my younger daughter. On the way home, I pick up my baby and then go home.

Liliana Teixeira (12)
Le Rocquier School, Jersey

The Monster Under The Bed

It was a bright and sunny morning, perfect for playing some footie in the park. So I got up and went downstairs to have my breakfast. I then asked my mum if she would give me a lift to the park. She said yes. I hopped in the car and off we went.

When I got to the park, I saw Paul, my best friend. So, I got out of the car and waved goodbye to my mum. Me and Paul played footie for hours, then it started to get dark.

'I had better go home,' Paul said.

'Why don't you sleep at mine?' I asked.

'OK,' he said, 'but I'll have to phone my mum.'

We went back to my house and Paul phoned his mum and she said it was OK for him to stay at my house. We went up to my room and played on my computer, then my mum came up the stairs and knocked on my door.

'Come in,' I said.

'It's getting late, better start getting ready for bed,' she said.

She left the room and we got in bed and fell asleep.

It was 12am when all of a sudden I was woken up by a loud creak that came from the floorboards under the bed. I peered under the bed and all I saw was two, big, bright blue eyes that looked liked sapphires. I jumped into my covers and woke Paul up.

'There's a monster under my bed!' I said.

'Let's see,' he said and he looked under the bed and screamed!

When I saw the eyes, I reached for my torch and flashed it under my bed.

The monster turned out to be our neighbour's cat, Fluffy!

Shaun Tadier (12)
Le Rocquier School, Jersey

Hercules

'Hades, your reign of terror ends here!' Hercules shouted as he ran towards Hades, pulling out his sword. Hades lifted his hands and a blue flame appeared over them.

'No, your life is over!' he replied, then threw the blue flame at Hercules. It struck him, sending him backwards into the sky.

'Pegasus, come here!' Hercules shouted quickly. Pegasus flew up to him and caught him.

'I don't have time for you!' Hades shouted. He turned around, whilst lifting his hands. A bluey-black swirl appeared and he walked into it and disappeared.

'Pegasus! Quick! Fly through that portal!' Hercules shouted. Pegasus squeezed in as it closed.

'Where is this?' Hercules asked.

Suddenly, something smashed into Pegasus, knocking Hercules to the ground.

'Huh? What was that?' he asked, before being kicked into a rock. He pulled himself up and could see Hades standing next to a giant, three-headed dog.

'This is my palace, the Underworld and this is my pet, Cerberus,' Hades said, menacingly.

Suddenly, the dog jumped to bite Hercules, but he had jumped up as well and was holding the mouth of Cerberus closed.

'You know some people say that a giant dog is real weight on your body and that weight could kill you!' Hercules shouted.

'And?' Hades asked, mockingly.

'That's what's happening to you!' Hercules replied.

Hades couldn't get another word in, before Hercules lifted Cerberus and threw him onto Hades, killing him. A wisp of blue smoke slid out from under Cerberus.

Miguel Coelho (11)
Le Rocquier School, Jersey

The Hydra

The Hydra was an evil myth, slayed by the Greek hero, Hercules. According to legend, it lived in the depths of Hell, coming out only to feed on those who challenged it.

The Hydra was a colossal beast. It was, in a way, unbeatable. Whenever someone cut off its head, two more appeared in its place. Its claws could have sliced right through Hercules. Its mouth was filled with razor-sharp teeth and could swallow many people whole.

In Greek, the word 'Hydra' means 'Serpent of Death'. It looked a bit like a snake.

Hercules alone couldn't overcome this monster, so he called upon his father, Zeus, king of gods, to help him slay the mighty Hydra.

Zeus sent a bolt of lightning crashing into a nearby cliff. This caused a deadly rock fall that crushed the Hydra underneath.

Hercules only survived due to the fact that the Hydra had him tight in its grasp. Hercules (and Zeus) had defeated the monstrous Hydra!

Jack Townsend (11)
Le Rocquier School, Jersey

The Murati!

The Murati was on the 14th of May, 2005. It was a sunny day and Guernsey and Jersey had a football match at Springfield Stadium.

It was all quiet in the first 15 minutes, but Jersey suddenly scored to make it 1-0. The crowd was cheering like they had never seen a goal in their whole lives. Jersey was cheering, but suddenly, Guernsey scored to make it one-all. Jersey then scored in the last couple of minutes of the first half, to make it 2-1 to Jersey.

It was 3.45pm and half-time. Jersey and Guernsey came through the tunnel and the crowd was cheering.

The game kicked off and Guernsey scored straight away. I could not believe it! Then it was coming up to the last 10 minutes of the game and Jersey scored, to make it 3-2! Everybody in the Jersey crowd was cheering, thinking it was all over, but in the last couple of minutes, Guernsey was cheering as they had scored! It was 3-3!

The atmosphere was burning when the game finished. Penalties were the way the game ended. It was 7-5 to Guernsey! I was so shocked!

Lisa Trehiou (12)
Le Rocquier School, Jersey

A Day In The Life Of A Cat

'Aawww!' That's me, yawning. I suppose it's time to get up. *Grrrr!* That must be my tummy, time for breakfast. Let's walk down the stairs and see if the humans are up to give me my breakfast.

I am now in the kitchen and to my surprise, my breakfast is already in my bowl!

Mmmm! Yummy! That was very tasty. I think I shall go outside for a stroll. I am now going to climb a tree, because that bird up there will make a tasty snack.

I am now in the tree about to approach the bird and pounce. I am now on top of the bird and all I have to do is tear it open and eat it. I have just killed the bird and I am in the process of eating it.

I have just finished the bird. It was alright I suppose, but it wasn't as meaty as I thought it was going to be.

I am now really tired. That day has used up all of my energy. I think it's time to go back to bed and see what tomorrow brings.

Stacey Mullins (13)
Le Rocquier School, Jersey

Rubbish Ruins!

In the parish of St Helier on Thursday 18th May, manual workers went on a two-day strike. Rubbish outside their store area began to mount. Extra trucks and many more things were being sent out to collect the extra rubbish that had been left for two days straight.

The manager, Dave Le Guyader, is concentrating on the scheduled Wednesdays' collections so that they don't fall behind.

The manager has decided to make a crew work during the afternoons of the working days, to clear the eurobins. This crew will have to work from 10am until 6pm on a three-month trial. However, two temporary staff members have been employed for a year. The manager says that this will not happen again.

Samantha Langlois (12)
Le Rocquier School, Jersey

My Day In The Classroom

Hi, my name is Frederick, but for short, you can call me Fred. I am a chair that sits in the corner of the classroom. My mother is called Mrs Stool and I have lots of friends. They like to jump on me and sit on me and that gives me really bad cramp. They sit on me for an hour each!

I have one enemy and he is called Scott Human and this is why I don't like him ...

1. He bounces on me when he is in class.
2. He farts on me all the time!
3. He once wet himself (I stank for days).
4. He always rocks on me and I am scared that he will break me.

At night I get really scared, as I get left all by myself and the caretaker walks around the room.

Once, I was in the classroom and a little boy started to rock on the chair next to me, but he slipped and broke my best friend, Winston Chairchill. I was so upset, I gave the little girls and boys wet bottoms for days, as my tears oozed onto the seat.

After a few months, new children come to the classroom from the lower years and they start to become my friends. The caretaker gave all the chairs and me, a nice, new pillow, so when someone sits on me, it doesn't hurt as much.

Mrs Stool starts her lesson soon so ... *goodbye!*

Zoë Samantha Dallimore (12)
Le Rocquier School, Jersey

A Day In The Life Of A Cat

'Oh, here she comes finally,' yawned the moggy, looking through the kitchen window. 'Honestly, if these humans knew how it felt to be locked out in the cold wind and rain, maybe I'd get a decent meal, instead of mouldy tuna and leftover scraps of Sunday roast chicken.'

The rather skinny cat jumped aside as the window was swung open by a pungent old lady, carrying a cup of hot chocolate in her shaking right hand.

'About time,' muttered the cat, under his breath, as he pounced through the window and landed right next to his food bowl.

'Eeww! Unfinished salmon from yesterday! This senile old bat doesn't have a clue about how to accommodate a species as important as me!'

The old lady slowly walked across the room and went back down the hall into the living room.

'Oh dear!' sniffed the cat. 'I think I've caught a cold.'

The cat walked out of the kitchen and down the hall and into the living room. The TV was on and the cat leaped onto the sofa, stepped around on the cushion for a few seconds, then finally dropped down. After all that eating, the cat was all tired out.

'Oh well, it might have been a lousy meal, but it'll only be a few hours before I get my next proper one! Maybe I should run away and find a different owner who can look after me properly. I know the poor old dear's probably not far off 200!'

Ben Moody (12)
Le Rocquier School, Jersey

A Day In The Life Of A Celebrity

I got up out of my king-sized bed. I then went downstairs to go to the kitchen, but got lost and ended up in one of the swimming pool rooms. I finally got to the kitchen and I had my breakfast.

I then got ready and that took me an hour and a half, because I have so many clothes, I don't know what to wear! I then got into my £200,000 car and went to my salon to have a manicure. My stylist then did my hair and make-up.

After that, I met up with my other celebrity friends and went out for lunch. We then went back to my house and went in my 17 feet deep swimming pool. We then went shopping for four hours.

My friends then went home and I had to go to work, I had to record a new song for my album. When I had finished doing that, I went back to my house and went in my self-tanning machine. I then had some tea and tried on my new clothes that I had bought.

After that, I went to my cinema (it's in my house!) and watched a film on my massive widescreen TV. Then I was really tired, so I went into one of my 26 bedrooms and watched telly for a bit. I then went to sleep.

Hannah Camsell (12)
Le Rocquier School, Jersey

A Day In The Life Of An Ant

Hello! My name is Ant. I have a family and I live in a big anthill with the other ants.

I was going for a walk and I was looking at the beautiful flowers, they were quite red, like blood. Then I saw a cherry tree that shone in the shining sun. The leaves shone like diamonds in the sky.

I was small, but that didn't matter to me, but then I got lost in the forest, so I slept in the cherry tree for the night. I could see the moon and it was shining brightly.

Then I tried to get home. It was a long way away and on the way I met a friend I hadn't seen in years. He was my old friend Ben the ant. We went to school together when I was a young ant. Then we walked home together and talked about the days when we were young ants.

When we got home, my wife was worried and my children were so happy to see me. My wife and kids were also happy to see my old friend. Everybody was drinking to celebrate.

Carla Pacheco (13)
Le Rocquier School, Jersey

A Day In The Life Of A Tree Frog

Hello, I am a tree frog, I live on the leaves of a Madagascar jungle. I sometimes have a good time, but the only problem is, I don't really see many other frogs around. People who are scientists, think that us tree frogs like to live alone, but my opinion is very different. I like to be with other frogs. One day, my life changed.

I went to my local swimming pool in the middle of some tall leaves, when suddenly, in the dark morning, I saw a small-shaped figure on the outside of my leaf. It was a noisy morning with the sound of crickets and lemurs. Anyway, I nervously adventured off my leaf to find another lovely, but chatty, tree frog.

He had nowhere to live, so I said that he could live with me and we could become friends. I had plenty of space in my home.

The next day, we got up and set off into the big world of Madagascar. I must say that that was the best day of my life. We climbed Madagascar's highest tree and we even made it into Madagascar's frog book of world records. We hope to stay best friends forever and ever.

Suddenly, I knew my whole life had changed. I felt like I was with my family again. As we ventured out the next day, a monkey picked me up. That wasn't a good sign, but my friend jumped onto his face and he dropped me. We ran away!

Rekina O'Regan (13)
Le Rocquier School, Jersey

Article One

In this article I'm not on top of a mountain, neither am I a shiny fish in the deep blue sea, or a still green chair in a classroom. I am an ordinary girl, living an ordinary life!

In my ordinary life, I go to school, I get home, but through all that, I look all around me and look at how happy people are! I compare them to all sorts of different people around this spectacular world, like in Kenya, where the children are so happy, even though they don't have a home to live in, or a school to get up to every morning. Neither do they have clean water to drink, but through all of that, you still see the smiles of their little, dry faces!

It sometimes makes you think, when you're walking down the corridor in school, why you see so many boys and girls, even teachers, that are so unhappy, when you know that they have all got a shelter to go to and food to eat and clean water and friends.

If you gave a football to the children in Kenya, they would worship that ball as if it were a god. They would play with it every day and never lose it. If you gave them something ordinary, they would make it extraordinary!

Read this article and think about it. This is my point of view, but you might have a different one. It doesn't really matter. You should live your life to the full and appreciate every little bit of it.

Tamsin Raine (13)
Le Rocquier School, Jersey

The Loch Ness Monster

In Scotland, a long time ago, lots of people loved to swim in their nearby lochs, but in one of the lochs, people were starting to disappear, but nobody knew.

One family had made a boat out of wood and they had two oars. They went down to the nearby loch, where people had been disappearing, put their boat in the water and got in.

They were in the centre of the loch, when they saw the water shake, then they heard a thump and out of the water, came a giant snake-like thing. It stared and stared at the family and then it ate the nan and snapped both oars.

The family were stranded with a great big snake in the middle of a loch! They decided that the only way they would escape was if they swam, but they weren't fast enough and were eaten.

Cullen Walsh (12)
Le Rocquier School, Jersey

A Soldier's Story

October 1940

Every day it is the same ... explosions, gunshots and screaming!

My name is Sam. I am 29 years old. I'm working for the army as an English officer. We are fighting the Germans. I have friends from France and America. I met them whilst fighting the Germans. I hate this war and it is the second war we have had in the last 50 years.

From day one, there has been sirens, gunshots (spraying over our heads) and explosions. We are in a trench in the middle of absolutely nowhere. I am covered in dirt. I have not had a hot bath for ages. All around me there are dead bodies, some are friends and some are enemies. They have had bullets pierced through them. Now, they are motionless.

We have nearly beaten the Germans, or so our captains tell us. We don't believe them, because they always say that. We are given disgusting food and inadequate rations. I hate this place. Tonight I am on sniper duty. That really annoys me, because people are sleeping (the ones that can I mean) while I have to make sure no one sneaks over to our trench and drops a bomb on us.

Why, is what I want to know. Why the fighting? Well, I know why, but that doesn't make it any better. Tomorrow will be the same. It's always the same.

2nd Regiment
France
30th September 1939

Dear Mother,

How are you? I hope you are well. It is hard here but I am surviving. Thank you for writing letters to me, it's what keeps me going. I have plenty of food and my spirits are high. How is the weather? The weather here varies from sunny to rainy and from hot to cold.

I don't think this war will last much longer. You never know, you might have me home next week. Not too many of us have died. Do not worry, I will be home soon.

Love Sam.

It is difficult to tell my mother the pain I feel inside and the physical agony every moment, because she is my mother and she shouldn't have to worry.

It was a terrible conflict. One that I do not wish to relive. The nightmares I have are terrible, they always contain guns, shooting and sirens. Let's hope they will ease soon.

David Bull (15)
Mount Tamar School, Plymouth

A Day In The Life Of A Pilot

It is early morning on the small island of Guernsey. Everything is quiet and peaceful near Guernsey's airport when suddenly a large and loud aircraft approaches and lands on the runway of the busy airport. Meanwhile a commercial pilot named John Blazer is waking up to a tiring and long day in the pilot business. John works for an airline company called Flybe.

John has to be at the airport at 10am for his departure to Birmingham International Airport. John arrives at Guernsey Airport at 9am; he needs to be there that early because he needs to have about 45 minutes (at least) for check-in and to be checked by security which he finds very boring and has 15 minutes for planning his flight.

John gets on his turbo-propelled aircraft, called a Dash, at 9am. He starts to taxi to the main runway with quite a large aircraft queue. It takes a long five minute wait and within that time John positions his long and large aircraft on the main runway. Suddenly, John thrusts up his engine throttle to full and John is in the calm and extraordinary cyan sky.

Within minutes John meets his planned out cruising altitude of 10,000 ft, watches out of the small cockpit window at the tiny island of Alderney. Fifty minutes later, John approaches the large airport of Birmingham and makes a smooth and successful landing. With two minutes of taxiing to his parking space, he is there ready to fly back home.

Ben Paice (13)
St Anne's School, Alderney

A Day In The Life Of A One Pound Coin

I woke up early that morning and was drained from the day before. The day was up and down like a roller coaster.

I was sitting, talking to my coin friends in the bank. I had been living there for a couple of days but it seemed like a lifetime.

Unexpectedly a huge monster of a hand came over me and grabbed me. Oh no! I was being moved. I couldn't stand it happening to me. I had just got comfortable and had made some good friends but now I was being taken away like an animal from the wild.

The next thing I knew I was put in a plastic bag and taken away. I was bumping up and down like I was on a bouncy castle and this didn't stop until I dropped like I had just jumped out of a plane.

I had landed in a dark, boring old purse, with just a 1p for company. It was boring.

Suddenly, the hand grabbed me, suffocating me. I couldn't breathe. I was then ferociously flung into a machine, which sang a song that gave me a headache.

I was sliding down, down, down, as coins were bashing into me, bruising in my skin. *Ting!* I landed on a shiny, silver surface. I was in a money machine.

That's where I am now, all alone at the bottom of what seems like a dark, empty pit. This time with no friends. Hopefully, someone will take me from here soon.

Sophie Hugman
St Anne's School, Alderney

A Day In The Life Of A Doughnut

It was a Monday. I hate Mondays. Everybody got free doughnuts on Mondays. Sixty boxes of doughnuts were going to get delivered to the nuclear power plant. It took an hour to get all 60 boxes to the power plant. I was in 'number three box'. All of the boxes got to the plant.

Box number one and two got opened. My box was just about to get opened but something happened. Someone opened my box and I fell out. I started to roll and I got faster and faster. One man called Homer Simpson saw me. He loved doughnuts no matter what. He could eat them for breakfast, lunch and dinner. He tried to grab at me but I got away. I was now in the darkest room and I did not know what to do. I rolled on but I hit something or someone. I looked and suddenly light came into the room. It was Homer. I tried to roll but I couldn't get away and he grabbed me. Then he put me into his mouth and the door closed.

Ben Morrell (13)
St Anne's School, Alderney

A Day In The Life Of A Pair Of Football Boots

It all started on the big day that was the cup final. Cristiano Ronaldo put me on before he started to train. After I was securely in place, he went out on to the pitch to train.

In training he had to run across the pitch 11 times, then he did some shooting, then he did some tackling. Then the whole team was called into the changing rooms because the manager wanted to talk to them about the match and that we had to win it.

The ref blew the whistle so we went out onto the pitch, but Cristiano did not start. He went on in the 80th minute and scored three goals so that Manchester Utd won the match.

Lee McCormack
St Anne's School, Alderney

A Day In The Life Of A Golf Ball

My life started at 4am on the last day of the big competition.

I was picked up by a huge, sweaty hand and was then put amongst five other golf balls. I had a large TW logo on my back, then I knew I was the ball that Tiger Woods, the world's best golfer, would use. I was eventually put in a gigantic golf bag. After a few turbulent rides for around five long hours of this annoying lad putting his hand and getting balls out of the bag.

Then it was my time to shine. I was hoisted out of the bag and put on a wooden peg. I scanned the area. I could see lots of people shouting and screaming, then I saw the leader board. It explained that Tiger Woods was actually winning the big competition. Tiger started to talk to his caddie about the weather conditions and then he put his club behind me, swung it, then *whack!* I was soaring through the sky like a bird. I could see trees, people and more golfers. I then looked down and saw the dreaded water. *Splash!* I was sinking to the bottom of the lake.

Matthew Capazario (13)
St Anne's School, Alderney

Worm War

On one July afternoon, there was a loud echo. At first it sounded like 'ghoul', but it was just me, Chris Moyle, shouting, 'Goal!' Me and my sister, Lisa, lived in a small street in Liverpool. Nothing ever happened there, it was really boring. 'That's 3-0 to Chris. And the crowd goes ...' I shouted.

Lisa interrupted me and said, 'No goal! You shot when I wasn't ready. That's not fair!'

I love it when I win, but Lisa hates losing. She just complains and says things like, 'I was looking at the birds fly past', or 'I was just combing my hair back'. She just can't take it.

Once, we were playing football at school and I headed the ball and scored. Then, obviously, she rejected my goal and said, 'You can't score by using your head! That's cheating!' She's such a wimp! She always plays as goalkeeper, but she moves out of the way when I kick the ball. Girls just can't play football.

Later on we both had to go inside. I then saw a long, slimy worm crawl along the grass. I hated bugs. I crushed them as soon as I laid eyes on one. Lisa saw what I was doing and tried to pull me inside. I simply pushed her away and lifted my foot and smashed it back down on the helpless little worm. Lisa then pushed me away and started to sulk. I gave a look of enthusiasm. Lisa said, 'I heard it's unlucky to kill something harmless. I hope it's true, you monster!'

Is she right?

Matt Knight (12)
St Anne's School, Alderney

An Unforgettable Day In The Life Of John Hathelright

It was the 10th April 1912; my wife and I were on our way to America. The RMS Titanic was the finest ship of its day, we were sailing from Southampton. It was a sunny April day and my wife and I were sitting on the top deck drinking wine looking at the sunset. I was blissfully unaware of the events that would follow.

After having dinner we walked around the deck, we couldn't help noticing that the water was so still that it looked like a giant mirror. We went back down to our cabin which was on C deck; we were delighted that you had to go down an elevator... on a boat! This was truly a marvel, no wonder the papers said that the ship was unsinkable as well as magical.

Later that night we heard a terrific crash and people screaming. We heard people running outside in the corridor and someone shouting, 'Come on, get your life jackets on, we haven't got all day!' My wife and I got our life jackets on and hurried to the deck only to find a lot of angry, screaming people. We really started to get worried at this point.

By now everybody knew that the boat was sinking and everyone was trying to get off the ship. I told my wife that we were going to be alright and that the White Star Line knew how to handle these things. Suddenly a man grabbed my wife and passed her into a lifeboat and told me to stand back because they were only taking women and children at this point and I was to go round and get another boat. But I found that all the boats were gone!

When the boats came back I was saved from the wreckage, I had survived by clinging on to a deckchair.

Paul Etheridge (13)
St Anne's School, Alderney

A Day In The Life Of Cristiano Ronaldo

08.00	Wake up thinking about game with Chelsea.
08.30	Had a big breakfast, which consisted of a healthy bowl of cereal to keep me fit and healthy.
09.00	Leave for Old Trafford - Manchester United's home ground, where I will train for two hours and 30 minutes.
11.30	Pep talk from Sir Alex Ferguson about today's game with Chelsea.
12.00	Game with Chelsea starts. I am playing striker.
12.30	Manchester United score from a corner. Paul Scholes scores.
12.45	Half-time, Manchester United winning 1-0.
13.00	Second half, Chelsea brings on a substitute. It is John Terry.
13.15	Chelsea score making it 1-1. Frank Lampard scored.
13.30	Manchester United score again from a free kick. I score.
13.45	End of match. Manchester United win 2-1. Paul Scholes is made man of the match.
14.30	Head home with girlfriend Tina and then have a long, relaxing bath and watch TV.
18.30	Head out for dinner at a posh restaurant called The Ivy. Tina orders a seafood dish and I order mussels and garlic bread. We both have Coke to drink.
22.30	Head to a posh nightclub where I meet up with some other footballers like Beckham and Michael Owen.
23.45	Just left the nightclub, still with my girlfriend.
12.00	Arrive home.
12.10	Watch more TV.
01.00	Bed.

Rio Bower (13)
St Anne's School, Alderney

A Day In The Life Of A Dog

I woke, stretched, yawned and pattered over to the stairs, where I whined until the human appeared. She scratched me on the back of my neck and walked into the kitchen. She reappeared with a bone! 'Woof,' I barked as I tore away at the juicy bone.

When I was finished, I needed to go outside, so I nosed the human's leg until she got up to let me out. I sniffed the air. Yum, next door were eating bacon! I found a tree, lifted my leg, walked back to the door and scratched it. The human came and opened it. I curled up by the roaring fire, my tummy still full and slept.

I was suddenly awoken by loud bangs. The human's parents were back! I cowered behind the sofa and shook. I waited, listening to the dreadful bangs and screams that the two drunks were making. I tried to sleep, but each time I closed my eyes, I had to reopen them for fear the humans were coming close.

Although I was scared, I mustered up the courage to go to my bowl to see if there was any food in it. It was rare that I got any dinner when the human's parents were around. Empty. I took a stride over to my water dish and licked, but it was empty. I tried to walk quietly back to my cosy bed, but I wasn't quiet enough. I heard footsteps behind me. A slipper was coming towards me!

Sarah Fuller (13)
St Ives Secondary School, St Ives

Potey And The Dragon's Eggs

Once upon a time there was a man who lived on a hill. His name was Potey. One day he went to the supermarket. He saw loads of things. He was looking around, when suddenly there was a stall with dragon eggs.

He bought two and went home. Potey looked after the eggs for one month and the dragons hatched. He called the boy dragon Perkey and the girl dragon Silvey. They were fire dragons.

Potey looked after them for five years and they grew to be big dragons. The boy dragon was a purple colour and the girl dragon was a yellow colour.

One day something strange happened. A fairy came to the house. She was talking to Potey and saying she needed help because she had lost her wand and it was in a cave of doom. Potey said, 'What do I get out of it?'

The fairy said, 'A castle and lots of money.'

Potey agreed to do her job.

The fairy teleported Potey, Silvey and Perkey to a wizard. He gave Potey a sword and some silver armour. Then the wizard said, 'Go to the cave of doom.'

The wizard gave a map to Potey. Potey followed the map with a compass and went to the cave of doom. Potey found an unlit torch. Perkey breathed out fire and lit it up.

Potey went further into the cave and came across an ogre. It was threatening Potey and it attacked him. Potey stabbed the ogre but the ogre looked at the wound and got his club and tried to knock Potey out. But the ogre missed and Potey stabbed the ogre in the head and the ogre died.

There was a light in the cave, so he went further in the cave and saw the wand. He picked it up and quickly ran out. But when he picked it up, loads of monsters came out of nowhere and chased them. Perkey and Silvey blew out a massive fireball. They were on fire! They were looking for water to throw over them to put to fire out, but they died. More monsters came out and Silvey blew out four fireballs and the monsters blew up. They finally came outside the cave.

The cave collapsed. The fairy was waiting outside the cave. Potey gave the fairy her wand and the fairy said some weird words. Loads of bags of money appeared and a castle appeared on the hill.

And they all lived happily ever after.

Sam Smith (13)
St Mary's School, Horam

The Mermaid And The Dolphin Rescue

Once upon a time there was a mermaid called Marina and a dolphin boy. They lived on an island called Mermaid Inn. It glowed with diamonds and rubies and was very pretty. They had a beach party where all their friends from all over the world came. There was a unicorn, a centaur and a magical face in the water. It glowed and talked and then took them back in time.

All the friends held hands and went round in the magic, glowing water. They went faster and faster and fell into a vortex. They went under the sea and through a tunnel and then it threw them up in the air and they landed in Egypt.

In Egypt they went to the Triangular Temple. It glowed with sequins and glitter, diamonds and rubies. They prayed to the sun god, Ra. They prayed for more water to swim in. As they left the temple, they walked along the hot sand and the mermaid and the dolphin flapped. They sank into the sand and found they were in Florida.

Marina and dolphin boy went to swim in the sea, while the others had a picnic on the beach. Suddenly, there was a tragedy. It all went bang and then black! The dolphin boy was stuck in a net and quickly taken away to a dolphinarium. There he had to swim with people. He hated it and squeaked for Marina.

Marina missed the dolphin boy and wanted to rescue him.

One night she sneaked in and set all the dolphins free. She opened the sea gates and told the ten trapped dolphins to swim free. 'Go out to sea,' she said, 'and have a nice life. Have lots of dolphin babies.'

She was so pleased to see dolphin boy again, but they had nowhere to live. They had to find somewhere where they wouldn't catch him again. So they lived in Florida in a hidden cove where there was lots of water for all the dolphins and especially dolphin boy.

Marina met a merman. They had two babies - one girl called Sparkle and one boy called Wave. They lived happily ever after.

So, if you're ever in Florida, you will know they are there, but please don't try to find them!

Melissa Ford-Nolcini (14)
St Mary's School, Horam

Hunting For Treasure

A long time ago, a boy and a girl called Tom and Mel found a map in their garden. It was a map of buried treasure on an island. They sailed to the island to find the treasure.

They found a pirates' camp. They ran to hide from the pirates who caught the children and took them down to a hidden camp underground.

They escaped because there was a hidden lever that led to a room full of treasure. They camped out. They did not get found and they got some treasure and escaped to the boat. They were happy to be going home with lots of gold.

Jake Crunden (14)
St Mary's School, Horam

The Smuggled Gold

One evening it was dusk. It was about time for the smugglers to come in on the boats to the smugglers' cave. When you are in the cave, you can see wet stone. You can hear drips of water. You can taste saltwater. You can touch cold rocks and you can smell stale seaweed.

When I was in the cave, I heard people coming, so I hid in a crack in the wall and I felt cold, scared and miserable. It was the smugglers.

They had loads of stuff in their arms but I could not see what it was. It was too dark where I was. It looked like bars of gold but I could not be sure.

About half an hour later they went out and I called my friend and told her to get down here. I gave her instructions on how to get down here. She said, 'OK.'

I said, 'Be careful,' and then suddenly my battery died so I got scared.

Later on she arrived and we went down the cave to find out more and when we got to the bottom of the cave we twigged what they were doing. They were smuggling gold to sell to people in this country.

So we went back up to the cave entrance but we had to hide because they were coming back! Once they had passed, we tried to get out of the cave but the tide was coming in fast, so we ran up the beach in the dark.

We got to the road and found the police were there. We told them what happened and the smugglers got caught gold-handed. They got a warning. They never did it again.

The smugglers said, 'If it wasn't for you two we wouldn't have been caught!'

The police said, 'Thank you. We have been looking for these four.'

Charlotte McRae (14)
St Mary's School, Horam

The City

The city slept. The eyes were closed, ears shut, nose blocked, mouth shut, senses covered by the silence outside.

A rocket had landed in the far Eastern part of the city. One, two, three, four, five. Five men walked off the ship. Each was silently weighed and measured without them knowing. The ears woke up, hearing the crunching of rubber boots over the cobblestone streets of the lost, lonely city, hearing every steady breath of the new, unknown men. The eyes had awoken, catching every movement of the men, their faces were white, their suits green, covering their whole body. The black rubber boots rising up and down with each step, their tousled hair waving slightly in the quiet breeze.

Now the rest of the city had awoken, the nose catching the smell of rubber boots, the smell of sweat on the necks of the men, the breath of each of them.

Finally, the brain awoke, taking in all sounds, tastes, smells and sights. By this time the five men had begun to get worried and started backing towards the ship to go back to Earth.

Suddenly, underneath them the ground opened and the men briefly saw a vast, mechanical cavern reaching out far beneath the silent city. At the next moment, all five hung upside down with their throats and chests cut open in long cuts.

The five men's organs were emptied onto a table and replaced with artificial ones made by the city. The five manufactured men marched back to their rocket, carrying five bombs to be released on Earth.

Connor Lawrence (13)
St Paul's Catholic College, Burgess Hill

Surfer Dudes

In northern Hawaii there was a group of friends who loved to surf and came to Maui for the day. They all knew each other from secondary school days and were all room-mates in Honolulu, southern Hawaii.

Chris, who had been surfing for most of his life, had surfed most of the biggest waves in the world. Jonny had just started to surf but had been in the Billabong and Quiksilver competitions. He had come first in both of them. James, who was probably one of the most successful and also one of the most experienced, had travelled the world to catch the biggest waves.

When Chris, Jonny and James were having their breakfast and listening to Surfer FM, they heard the presenter say: 'In Maui today at 9.25am there is going to be a 150ft wave.' Chris, Jonny and James could not believe it. They looked at each other in disbelief.

James said to Jonny, 'Do you want to go and surf it?'

Jonny replied, 'Why not? Let's go!'

'Come on, Chris, we will be in the car,' shrieked Jonny.

Coochuka the car started with a loud bang and splutter. Chris ran down the stairs and jumped in.

An hour later they arrived at the beach.

'Wow guys, look at the waves,' exclaimed Jonny.

'James, pull over in this lay-by,' said Chris.

'Quick, let's go and catch some of the biggest waves in the world!' they shouted together.

The three surfers jumped out of the car and ran down the hill. Chris and James jumped into the sea and paddled out.

'Come on Jonny, come in,' said James in excitement.

'Coming,' replied Jonny.

Chris and Jonny were about half a kilometre out when they noticed a storm brewing on the horizon. The boys all looked at each other anxiously.

'Well, we are here now so we might as well ride the waves for a bit longer,' said Jonny.

'Yeah, might as well,' replied Chris and James.

They did not have to wait long until an awesome wave built up behind them. The boys used all their strength to get into position.

'Wow! Look at that wave - that must be at least a 100 footer,' shouted Chris.

'Get on your boards and start paddling like mad!' said James.

The power of the wave took them to their feet. The roars of the waves filled their ears. The boys felt a mixture of fear and exhilaration as they skimmed along to the shore. A crowd of people standing on the beach watched in astonishment, clapping and cheering. As the friends got to their feet, they patted each other on the back and agreed that there would never be another wave like that again.

Jonathan Pickering (12)
St Paul's Catholic College, Burgess Hill

Shark Attacks Surfer

Yesterday three surfers were out surfing in Australia. As you know it is the time of year, currents are strong.

Dan and Andy went out whilst Alex fixed his board. Alex was watching. He looked down at his board, he looked back and they were gone.

'I thought maybe they had moved along the beach, so I carried on'. It wasn't until 20 minutes later he panicked.

Suddenly, Andy came out from under the water.

'I could just see Andy's head out of the water with a surfboard and something on it,' said Alex.

Andy pushed the board onto shore. Dan had been attacked by a shark. Alex ran and got the ambulance.

'We were surfing and suddenly Dan went down. I thought it was strange because he wouldn't normally bail on a 30 foot wave. I swam down after him - it was then I saw him floating and the shark swimming away. I went down and brought him up to the surface and swam him into shore'.

Dan spent three months in hospital and had two operations to remove the shark's teeth and fix his bones. He is now happy at home with only scars to tell the tale and is back surfing three times a week.

They have sent experts to find body parts left from the attack.

Josh Gentry (13)
St Paul's Catholic College, Burgess Hill

Buckingham Break-In

At 1am this morning two figures masked in black entered the royal premises and attempted a robbery. There was only one guard who saw them and he states, 'They seemed to appear out of nowhere'.

The burglars stole exactly two bottles of wine from the kitchen and a pillow from the bedroom. Luckily, no one was present at the palace.

The chief of police said, 'This is the most peculiar break in I have ever experienced'.

The police sent two burglar detectives down into the sewers. They have found no traces of them whatsoever.

A former burglar, Bill Sibbly, was sent onto the crime scene and found a possible entrance and exit. He says that there is a secret passage through the cupboard attached to a wall.

The passage was studied by professional historians, Anne Will and John Simmo, and they say that this was most probably used by soldiers to escape at times of siege in the Middle Ages.

Traces of the pillow that was stolen were found in the passageway, thus showing that the burglars used this way to get in and out.

The burglars moved out of the passageway and across the grounds, then to be seen by the guard.

The police arrested two twenty-six year-old men. One of them shouted, 'I didn't do nuffin'!' The other one remained silent.

John Cannon (12)
St Paul's Catholic College, Burgess Hill

Mum, Dad, Where Are You?

It was 2nd June 1939 as I was getting ready for school, when all of a sudden Mum called me into the lounge. I said to her, 'What are you doing?'

She replied, 'You are not going to school today as the war is going to begin any day now and we have to take you down to the coast, to the town hall in Seaford.'

I ran to my bedroom and the tears just rolled down my face, while I was packing a bag. I was supposed to go to Lindsay's house tonight. I sat there on my quilt holding this picture of Mum and Dad on their wedding day and my cousins who are now 27 and 31. Then Mum came to help me.

We caught the 9.27am train from London. We arrived at what looked like a haunted old building. I hugged my mum and dad for maybe the last time ever, or perhaps just for a while, no one could tell. A lady and gentleman came and said, 'Is this one cute enough, Derek?'

Who me? I thought. I was overwhelmed as I was going to a family who really thought a lot about me. Then, as I looked back, there were my parents waving goodbye to me. I started to cry and my new parents handed me a lacy handkerchief and wiped my eyes. They also gave me a hug and introduced themselves: 'I'm Georgina and this is Derek. We are pleased to meet you.'

I started to look worried and began to feel alone, but my new parents were very nice and they took me home in a horse and trap and soon I felt at home.

Helen Coates (12)
St Paul's Catholic College, Burgess Hill

A Day In The Life Of A Second World War Soldier

It's the 6th of June 1944 and you are saying goodbye to your family and friends, not knowing what is ahead of you. You are with other men who you will fight with against the enemy, in order to help your country and many others in the world. You board ships heading towards the beaches that will be like graves for the men, who don't know how bad it will be. You arrive and stop near the beaches. There is death already and the sea turns red with blood, like strawberry jelly not set.

This is in France, on the beaches of Normandy, Omaha, Utah, Gold, Juno and Sword, with guns firing at you, mines below you, planes above you and sea behind you. Those who make it out of the sea head their way up the beaches towards the towns and cities of France you are determined to liberate.

But before you can do this, you have to face bunkers with deadly guns and fight against other men. All you can hear are mines exploding and tanks rumbling and voices shouting for help. The sight is too bad to tell. The thoughts and emotions you have are unexplainable and what you have seen and heard, you never want to speak of again. All you want and think of now is staying alive and peace forever from now. Happiness and joy.

Rhiannon Parton (12)
St Paul's Catholic College, Burgess Hill

Life

Lucy couldn't concentrate. Her mind was full of excitement. Today was a Monday and usually most children hated Mondays but she didn't, she loved them. Every Monday at four o'clock she went horse riding. She always rode a horse called Zebadee. Zebadee was a 15.2hh strawberry roan. She couldn't wait until four o'clock.

'Hiya Lucy,' her best friend May called as she walked briskly to the hall.

'Oh hi,' Lucy replied.

'So what have you got first lesson then?'

'Uh?'

'So?' May questioned.

'I don't know, leave me alone.' And with that Lucy walked off.

'Something's wrong with Lucy,' May explained to Laura in a concerned voice.

'Well, it is a Monday and she's going horse riding,' replied Laura fiddling with her hair.

'Anyway, Lucy's got to stop freaking out about horse riding, it's really getting on my nerves,' May announced and at that very moment Lucy walked past.

'So you think I'm annoying do you!' Lucy screamed.

'No, it's just ...'

'Shut up, I don't want your excuses, I hate you!' And she ran off crying.

When Lucy got home she was in a bad mood. She never thought that loving horses so much bothered anyone. She didn't care though. 'I don't need anyone - just horses,' she said to herself.

Even by the time she got out of school, she was still mad. As she got out of the car when they arrived at the stables, her Dad smiled and said, 'Go break a leg, Lucy.'

'Shut up Dad and get a life, you're so embarrassing!' she said as she stomped off in a huff.

'Right, now approach the triple in a brisk canter,' shouted the riding instructor at the end of the school.

'Come on, Zeb,' whispered Lucy. At the corner she popped Zebadee on into a canter. She forgot suddenly what she was doing and heard May's voice in her head. *It's so annoying,* the voice echoed over and over again.

'Lucy!' the riding instructor shouted. 'Lucy!'

But it was too late. Lucy flew off Zebadee and head first onto the pole in front of her. She couldn't move and seconds later Zebadee was on top of her, squeezing the air out of Lucy's lungs. That day she was put into hospital. That day she died.

The moral of this story is - live each day as if it's your last. Always be friendly to everyone around you because you don't want it to end on a bad note.

Sophie Hunt (11)
St Paul's Catholic College, Burgess Hill

The Turtle's Selfishness

(Based on one of Aesop's fables)

Ever wondered why turtles have their home on their backs? Well it all started a long time ago when the turtles didn't have shells.

One day in the humid, tropical jungle there lived a radiant turtle. He lived with his best friend Emma, a hummingbird. She was very clever.

A powerful, wise wizard lived in the jungle. He was getting married to a princess. He sent out invitations to all the animals, from the tiny bugs to the herds of elephants.

When the turtle got his invitation he wasn't happy like all other animals. He just wanted to stay in his house and watch the fish in his lagoon. Emma was furious; she was going to go with or without him. 'Emma, will you tell the wizard I'm ill?' shouted the turtle as Emma was fluttering out of the door. She couldn't believe how selfish he was. She wasn't going to lie for him.

At the party she told the wizard and princess why the turtle wasn't there. 'He just couldn't be bothered,' she explained. The wizard was extremely angry. Emma told him he should teach him a lesson and that is what he did.

Afterwards, the wizard went round to the turtle's house. He told him how disappointed he was but the turtle didn't care, so the wizard got out his wand and swished it around in the air. Suddenly, the turtle's home and lovely lagoon was gone. On the turtle's back was a big, heavy shell. Emma exclaimed, 'You shouldn't just think of yourself. Think of others and give and take.'

The turtle forgave her and they still remained best friends. He was able to go anywhere he wished to from then on, as he always had his home with him.

Ellie Wood (12)
St Paul's Catholic College, Burgess Hill

A Day In The Life Of An Arsenal Supporter

The smell of boiled cabbage wafted through the hotel, but it did not dampen our spirits, as it was the FA Cup Final against Manchester United.

We left the hotel wearing our Arsenal shirts and scarves and headed off to the Millennium Stadium in Wales. We arrived at Cardiff with thirty minutes to spare. I was really excited, as it was the first time that I had ever seen a cup final. The stadium was packed to the limit with Arsenal and Manchester United supporters. I started to get really nervous as we were missing one of our best players.

The first half went really quickly and Manchester United had all the play and all the shots on goal. Arsenal only had one shot on goal but it did not even go close. The Manchester United fans were getting louder and louder, sensing a victory was in their grasp.

The players came out to a big roar from their fans and the second half began. Midway through the second half I was starting to get really nervous. Manchester United had hit the post twice in the space of two minutes. I could hardly look.

The second half ended with a dramatic close, it was still 0-0. The game had to go into extra time.

Very little happened in extra time as the players were exhausted and the score remained 0-0. This meant that penalties had to be taken. This was the first ever penalty shoot-out in the history of the FA Cup.

The tension in the stadium was growing as Manchester United had missed one of their penalties. Arsenal had one more penalty to take. If the player scored then they would be champions of the FA Cup.

As the player approached the penalty spot, I had to close my eyes as I could not bear to watch. I held my breath, the stadium went quiet. A few seconds later a huge roar ripped through the Arsenal fans. The player had scored! *Arsenal had won the FA Cup!*

Ian Bowtell-Sims (12)
St Paul's Catholic College, Burgess Hill

The Battle Of The Last Human Land

Duur was standing beside one of the many gates in the fort of the human lands. He was a guard there, protecting the king's halls. Today was a lot different to him though. Battle was approaching the city. The monster demons were attacking the last of the human lands. The humans had to last.

As the demons moved into view, bells started sounding throughout the city, warning the women and children to get into the keep. The soldiers got ready into their positions, along with Duur who stood at the top of the wall waiting.

The demons began to charge around 100 feet from the front wall. Suddenly, out of nowhere, appeared hundreds of ladders made from dust in their hands. Then appeared about 50 trebuchets in the path behind them. Six hundred human cavalry were sent out of the front gate to attack at that moment and looked tiny compared to the 100,000 demons they were approaching. Was it the end for the last surviving humans in the land?

As the cavalry attacked, archers fired clouds of arrows upon the enemy, at which time Duur and 1,000 other troops were ordered onto the battlefield to what seemed like the end for them.

As the battle progressed, Duur fought ferociously, killing many foes, when he saw thousands of ally foot-soldiers at the top of the hill. He felt extremely relieved at the sight of friendly elf, dwarf and gnome allies from distant lands charging into enemy lines. It was easily the end for these demons, but many more would come. The allies had to stick together to survive. But at the moment, they should just wait.

Will Pearson (13)
St Paul's Catholic College, Burgess Hill

Crime Scene Investigation

I was called on a matter of urgency and secrecy. It was cold and raining in Los Angeles. I was solving the brutal murder of an unknown child. The child's face was torn from his skull with teeth marks and chunks from the corpse lying in a puddle of blood.

It was hard trying to figure out who he was. We soon identified him by his dental records and fingerprints. He was identified as Antony Petersham. After a post-mortem examination and forensics had finished, it was easy to see this had been done by no normal creature.

Before we had a chance to come to our conclusion, we had six phone calls saying people had been attacked and killed and many more injured by an animal of massive size with razor teeth which tore the flesh from their bodies.

We then phoned around every zoo in New York and the surrounding cities. They all had their animals and we had no idea what to do - whether to send out a search party or advise everyone to stay in their homes.

Later, a member of my forensic team found animal blood and did some tests. She found that it was contaminated with oil and nuclear waste and was a cheetah's blood. I was stumped - there were no cheetahs anywhere near New York or anywhere else in North America. Then it hit me! The circus was in town. They had cheetahs and were right next to a nuclear power plant. Now all we needed to do was catch it! We set a trap in Central Park. We caught it, tranquilized it and gave it back to the circus where it soon died.

Oliver Phillips (13)
St Paul's Catholic College, Burgess Hill

A Day In The Life Of Cherisse (The Faders)

7.30am - I'm so tired. Last night we all went to a party at one of Molly's friend's house. There was loads to eat and drink and hundreds of people to talk to. Molly introduced me to a few of her other friends; they were all real nice. We partied all night until 1am, which wasn't good cos we are recording our new single 'Jump', which I don't feel like doing right now!

8.30am - We're in our van on the way to the studio now. I've perked up after a bit of breakfast. Molly is in a bad mood. Toy said she fell out with one of her friends last night. I'm looking forward to recording; I can really take out any anger I have on my drums. Sometimes I hit them so hard, it makes a huge dent in the skin! Whoops!

9am - Now we are here, it's best to get on and set up, mic check!

9.30am - All done, now for rehearsal.

10am - Wow! I'd forgotten how good Molly can sound singing to the backing track and Toy strumming away on the guitar. It feels really good to get back to music. I'm so hungry, I think I need a packet of Cheetos, yum.

11.15am - Right, now to get down to business. Recording's up next. Let's hope I don't drop my drumstick like last time. I was practising spinning it around my hand and dropped it when I was supposed to be drumming.

12pm - Finally finished. We messed up twice... more like the amp did. It kept mucking Toy's guitar up. Now we can go home and relax. I need to do some food shopping and I need some new clothes. See you in a little while.

3pm - I spent ages clothes shopping. I saw so many things I liked: tops, bags, jackets, boots and some jewellery too. I bought mainly everything I saw. I got some stuff for Toy and Molly too. Jeans and belts and stuff like that. Now I need to catch a bus home, I really need an extra pair of hands.

4pm - Home at last. I need food. No lunch doesn't do wonders for my stomach. Toy, bless her, ordered a pizza, should be here any minute. I love pepperoni and melted cheese after a hard day's work.

4.12pm - Mmm. Pizza is good. The rest of the evening I'm gonna watch TV. I love a scary movie too. I'm going channel surfing.

11pm - I think my eyes have gone square! Six hours and 45 minutes of TV! I'm going to bed. Remember, it's a Faders world.

Becky Bates (12)
St Paul's Catholic College, Burgess Hill

A Dare

A collage of autumn-coloured leaves crunched underneath our feet. Tammi and me, I mean. I'm Angela and everyone always mixes us up because we are twins and we look almost identical with our long blonde hair and tall, skinny figures. We are three minutes apart and currently both fourteen. Now we are entering the so-called haunted forest! It is cursed by some girl who killed herself in here to get away from bullying. Blahdy, blahdy, blah, who cares? It is so fake, just to scare us!

So that is the myth, that anyone who comes in here will never return! The ghost will catch you! How stupid is that?

'Isn't this stupid? They all think we won't return from this stupid gathering of trees and mud,' Tammi said, awaking the silent woods.

'Yeah, I know. Did you see their faces when we left?'

We were silent again and that's when I heard it - the sound of a voice; a girl whispering curses and violent threats.

'Angela, do you hear something?'

'No,' I said, although this was a lie.

The voices bounced from all the trees, the whispering threats getting louder each second.

We walked on and I seemed to be seeing things. All I remember is one minute I was walking and the next minute Tammi's scream pierced the quiet forest. I saw an approaching image of a girl with long black hair. She had a face covered in scars and her dark eyes were filled with hatred. I felt a sharp stab of pain and then everything went black.

I woke up, my head spinning. My face was throbbing and I hurt all over. I looked around me, managing to sit up. White, white, white, plain white and emotionless, like a blank piece of paper with nothing written on it. I saw machines and charts all around me. I realised I was in hospital. I saw Tammi, her face was as plain as the hospital walls, it matched her fluffy white pillow. As Mama used to say when we were little girls, her hair looked like an angel's sash upon a fluffy cloud. I never liked the thought of being a sash on some cloud. I thought Tammi looked like a china doll - hair spread across a pillow looking peaceful. I think she looks dead. It was a dare that led us to be here. A dare.

Anna Martorana (13)
St Paul's Catholic College, Burgess Hill

Lost And Found

They were tired; they hadn't eaten a scrap of meat for what seemed to the cubs like hours. Lupus, their father's oldest son, had escaped with his younger siblings away from the fire; they had been separated from the rest of the pack when a tree engulfed by flames had fallen. Lupus set off in search of shelter...

They finally reached a cave. Lupus scented the ground, then stepped into the cave, leaving the cubs outside. He pounced just before his prey could escape, killed it and went for the rest. In a few minutes he had caught four baby rabbits and their mother. 'Brackle, Thorn, Zebie, come and eat,' Lupus said with a proud grin and a bark of excitement. After the young ones had eaten, they promptly fell asleep and Lupus soon followed.

In the morning Lupus caught three small rodents and had them for breakfast with Brackle, Thorn and Zebie. They started to search for home, with Lupus leading the way. Lupus used instinct to find his way; he looked for paw prints, he listened, he scented the forest around him, but found nothing. The cubs were silent so their big brother could concentrate, but they soon gave this up when they wanted food...

It was getting dark and suddenly, 'I've got it...' shouted Lupus. With a new hope the cubs hastily ran after him as he raced away. But surprisingly, Lupus was not the one who found the wolves, it was Ryan, their uncle. They greeted each other with cries of joy. Ryan took them home and both Lupus and cubs ran to greet their family.

That night the pack feasted. Sleepily, the cubs snuggled near their parents' warm fur. Lupus stared into the face of the moon and then said a silent *thanks* ...

Ruth Morley (13)
St Paul's Catholic College, Burgess Hill

A Day In The Life Of Steven Gerrard

The life of Steven Gerrard is a bit hectic!

In the morning he has to wake up at about six because he has to eat breakfast and then go straight to football training. His training takes all day so he does not have much time for anything else. Steven sometimes has meetings with Rafael Benitez to talk about training and the team, because Gerrard is the captain.

Gerarrd arrives at Melwood in the morning where he sits down with the whole team and they have their breakfast together. This is usually salads and food with high energy levels.

From there he goes with the team to begin their warm-ups for their training sessions.

After training he usually plays in a practice match with the other players before doing the warm down. Some days he also goes to the club gym if he feels like doing some extra strength training. The gym at the new Melwood is five times bigger than the gym at the old Melwood.

After training he goes into the signing area. Fans have shirts and balls because they belong to Liverpool Football Club and people want things signed all the time.

In the relaxation room he relaxes in the jacuzzi because Benitez does not like the players to go anywhere after training.

The treatment room is portable so players can take it to home games.

In the recreational facilities there are pool tables, table tennis and lots more. The team is in this room a lot because Benitez likes the foreign players to mix with the British players.

Jenna Bell (13)
St Paul's Catholic College, Burgess Hill

... And Then She Fell Before My Eyes

Sara Richards, 14, and her cousin Amy, also 14, were best friends. That was until she saw her darker side ...

We'd been begging our parents to let us go late night shopping at Flowerfields shopping centre for ages. 'It would be totally safe,' I told my mum. She and my aunt finally agreed to let us go, but as long as we were back by 12. We were so excited! But when I said it would be totally safe, I couldn't have been more wrong ...

After exhausting every single shop we could find, we started walking home. It was 11.45, but it would only take 10 minutes to get home, or so we thought. Suddenly, I heard a noise, like purring. I turned sharply. Nothing. But then I couldn't find Amy. I was terrified. I tried her mobile. No one picked up. My heart thudded in my chest. Suddenly, I heard a blood-chilling scream. I ran so quickly, I almost tripped over. But I had to find Amy ...

Then I found her - with something. I'm still not sure what, but its teeth were sinking into her neck, blood dripping to the floor. Then he drew back and she fell before my eyes onto the pavement. Slowly his hungry amber eyes focused on me. I did what any person would have done - I ran!

It was 12.30 when I got home. When my mum saw me, she had a face like thunder. 'What time is it? And where's Amy?'

I started sobbing. 'Amy's dead!' I cried and sank to the floor howling.

We never did find Amy's body, even though I took my parents back to the alley. I feel sick thinking what that thing did to my cousin ... and I don't want to find out ...

Charlotte Heeney (12)
St Paul's Catholic College, Burgess Hill

The Magic Calculator

One Hallowe'en night at 9pm and there stood five children in the darkness of Brighton Lane. They were playing a game of truth or dare, when one of them dared me to enter the old, abandoned house at the end of the lane.

I walked into the mist of the night where the old house stood. I went to the front of the house where a gigantic wooden door stood. I opened the door and it creaked quietly. I walked in and found it wasn't as big as it looked from the outside. I explored the downstairs of this derelict house slowly, but there wasn't anything that scared or amazed me that much. I then thought I would explore the upstairs of the house. The wooden stairs creaked and I walked up.

The upstairs was almost all bedrooms. I entered the bedrooms and bathrooms and also a study. I entered a bedroom with an ensuite which looked to be the main bedroom because it was larger than the rest. After this I had just one more room remaining until I had completed this dare. I was just about to leave the last remaining room when a strange-looking wardrobe caught my eye. I opened the wardrobe and saw what looked like a calculator. I thought I would check if it worked and typed in 7 minus 2. Suddenly, I found myself in the same park that I was in exactly five hours ago!

I looked at my watch and saw it was 4pm. I then typed in 3 plus 2 and found myself back in the old, abandoned house at 9pm. I put the calculator down and ran out of the old house and back to my friends.

Benjamin Simpson (12)
St Paul's Catholic College, Burgess Hill

Guys, Who Needs Them? Girls Do!

I'm on the beach listening to the waves, thinking about him but why? He is only a guy and normal in fact, but I can't stop thinking about him. His nice blond hair that looks cute when it's in the sunlight and his eyes, blue like a diamond floating on water. My thoughts were interrupted by my mates.

'Hi,' said Ashley and Davina. By the way, they're mad and my name is Suzie. 'What you thinking?' they both said together.

I just laughed and told them it was nothing. We started to walk to school even though it was a Saturday. You see we were going back to England, to a place called Burgess Hill. I was really excited but also nervous to go back and also I couldn't wait. We were here at last.

'No one move, you are all now going to be taken to a school called St Paul's and are going to stay there,' a man shouted when we got off. We thought this was something the teachers had put on, but we were far from right. They were evil criminals. They locked us in a hall together.

A few minutes later there was a little rustle by the window. It was Alex. I was so happy to see him again. We told everyone to get out of the window where he had just made a hole in it. He told us it was safe, we just had to go down the rope where everyone else was. So we did and then he took us out of there. We had to get out quickly before they found out we were gone. When everyone was safe, we started to go back to the place where we were staying, but that wasn't it. One of the evil men was my cousin Daniel and I saw him. I knew what I had to do so I ran back. Alex followed. We told everyone else to go and go quickly and they did. We had some unfinished business to do.

We caught up with Daniel and fought him with some swords we had found. The swords went one way, then the other, then he smacked them out of our hands, so we had to use our fists. We then smacked his sword out of his hand, so he also had to use his fists too until we got him down on the ground. Alex tied his hands together with some rope so he couldn't get away.

We took him to the police station and they put him in a cell, then quickly we went to see the others. When we got there, everyone greeted us. We were so happy to be safe again.

Suzanna Marlow (12)
St Paul's Catholic College, Burgess Hill

A Day In The Life Of A Child At War

I woke up this morning and felt something was going to happen today. I went downstairs for breakfast. Mum was making breakfast, Dad was reading the newspaper and Tom was sitting at the dining room table eating his breakfast, reading his favourite book. Mum told me that she had to get the weekly rations from Bob's corner shop down the road. She said I could go with her, so I collected the coupon books from the cupboard and we went out with our gas masks in our bags. Then the sirens went off. We all hurried into the air raid shelter that Dad had dug in the back garden.

I was sitting there so scared of what was going to happen next. Would the shelter fall down on us? Would the Germans win the war? No one knew. There was a long silence. We couldn't hear any bombs falling or the engines of the planes above us, and the only noise around us was the rustling of the trees outside.

Mum said we'd be here until tomorrow, so I had a sleep. It was so small in the air raid shelter. My big brother, Tom, and I had to share the old sofa. My dad moved it down here when he realised that the bombing wasn't going to go away.

I was feeling a bit sorry for myself because we were in a war, but then I realised I was lucky because I didn't get evacuated out to the country.

Finally, the all clear sounded and we all went out onto the street to see if our neighbours had survived - some people didn't. This time we were lucky, but next time - who knows?

Charlotte Newell (12)
St Paul's Catholic College, Burgess Hill

The Sea Horse

The high-pitched whinny came again that night. It had come at the same time for three nights. Lila lay picturing the events of the last few days, the vision of a white shape, the dream and the high-pitched whinny. It seemed so strange. It somehow linked together.

4am - a perfect time to creep down to the beach where the strange things had happened. She gathered her coat, a torch and pulled the dog out of its basket. The dog was not to help her, just for comfort. They set off. Clouds of mist swept like a cloak over the night sky.

Just as she was about to give up, after fifteen minutes, the blinding light of the white shape came into view. But it was not tall and proud, it was crumpled on the sand. Then she realised it was a horse. A sea horse appeared from the white waves. She bent down beside it, cuddling it close to her. *'Lila,'* she felt it say, making her feel dizzy. It spoke again saying, 'Put sea water in my eyes! I am blind! It will heal me and help me get back to the sea.' She did so. It smiled, stood up proud and tall and galloped into the whites of the waves.

The waves then spelt the words, 'thank you'.

Clea Roberts (12)
St Paul's Catholic College, Burgess Hill

It Was Just A Dream

My fingers are black and my knuckles are swollen from the coldness of the air I breathe. I wait at the door - *knock, knock, knock,* I hear footsteps coming towards the door. The floorboards creak from the heaviness of the feet, the handle of the door turns. As it opens I see black. I enter and cobwebs blow in my face, spiders crawl all over my head. I get shivers down my spine as I see fire. I hear a voice, it says, 'Go through the door and don't, I repeat don't, take any more steps. Don't, don't, don't ...' More and more it fades away, more and more. I become frightened. I know somebody is watching me although I cannot see them and then *bang!* I turn around and I see black spots in front of my eyes. I run for the exit, but the door is locked. I kick at the door. I kick so hard, my shoelace snaps. I start to panic and I scream so loud that it echoes all through the house. I run around frantically looking for an exit, but then I see it - a broken window. I crawl out of it onto the cold, wet grass. I run as fast as my legs will carry me - all the way home. Then I finally get back into bed and I wake with a cough. My heart is pounding and then I realise, it is only a dream - a dream.

Amy Roberts (11)
St Paul's Catholic College, Burgess Hill

A Day In The Life Of Commander O'Shovah

Deep in the eastern fringe of the galaxy, a race so technical for its time emerged out of nowhere. No science behind it, they thought now was the time for their race. The race was TAU.

The leader, Commander O'Shovah, wanted the galaxy and he thought he could have it, with the technology of their rail guns and their pulse rifles, he thought he was invincible. But as every army tried, none triumphed.

The TAU had been building their army training and developing all the weapons they could. For instance, the rail gun is a huge weapon that could only be transported by the crisis battle suit, but now can be transported by the pathfinder snipers. The crisis battle suit, without development it can't fly, but it can now because of the new jet packs. This may not win the battle, but it can help them to.

Now they are heading to Cyrene to attack the Necron, but they are one of the hardest armies to kill, so they may not succeed.

As they land they are confronted by a squad of Wraiths on a hunt. They send a message to the city. Commander O'Shovah jumps at them and destroys them. He sends his army to the city in extreme hope of triumph.

Ten years later, Commander O'Shovah's troops are not hopeful anymore. This is a never-ending war. In the grim darkness of the 41st millennium there is only war.

Jamie Thompson (12)
St Paul's Catholic College, Burgess Hill

The Curse Of Tutankhamun

Abdullah wrenched the door open with a breathtaking heave. A roar of musty, stale air was thrust into his face as he finally entered the ancient tomb of Tutankhamun. Untouched cobwebs hung abandoned from the ceiling and piles of Egyptian gold were cluttered on the cold stone floor.

Father would have given his life to be standing here, Abdullah thought sadly. He crept past all the treasure to the thing *he* most wanted to see. Draped with shadows in the corner of the tomb was a filthy casket. The detailed carving of a young boy was displayed on it. Abdullah was shivering uncontrollably by now. Excitement flooded every bone in his body, every tooth in his jaw. With a rush of pure adrenaline, he threw the delicate lid open to find ... nothing. Absolutely zilch. The pharaoh was gone. All the effort he had forced into the discovery of this wonder suddenly went right down the drain. All the sacrifices ...

He was interrupted in his disgusted thoughts by an angry growl behind him. *Oh no,* Abdullah thought. He had forgotten all about the curse of Tutankhamun's tomb and as he slowly turned round, his lips curled into a blood-curdling scream ...

Andrew Brown (12)
St Paul's Catholic College, Burgess Hill

A Day In The Life Of A Dog

3am	Wake up and scratch fleas.
3.05am	Get bored and bark for attention.
3.10am	No results so bark louder.
3.15am	Got a few 'shut up, Teds' but that's not what I want. Bark louder still.
3.30am	Jim comes down, puts food and water in my bowls. I stop barking and eat.
4am	Liz comes downstairs and starts to make Matt his lunch for the day. I move in and out of her legs whining. She knows I want my walk but pretends not to, so I head towards my empty food bowls and whine. This sees some quick results and I'm eating in no time.
7am	Matt comes down. He shows me attention. He goes to eat breakfast. I go to sleep.
8am	Walkies! Me and Liz take Matt to school, then she takes me to the park.
8.40am	After thirty minutes of pointless running after a tennis ball, I am back home. Liz and Jim are at work and Matt's at school. I head for my basket and start to chew my chewy bone.
10am	Go to sleep and dream about mountains of bones.
3pm	Wake up, head to chair by window to wait for Liz and Matt.
3.45pm	They're home. I give them a welcome only a dog could.
4pm	Eat food Liz has put out for me.
5-7pm	Muck around with toys and various other things.
7.01pm	Go to sleep.
3am	Wake up. Scratch fleas ...

Joe Buglass (13)
St Paul's Catholic College, Burgess Hill

Don't Leave Me!

I clutched my mum, but she insisted I had to go. The year was 1940 and World War II had just begun. The government was sending all children into the country to be safe. I didn't want to go, although I knew I had to. I hesitated when getting on the train, every few seconds looking back to see if my mum was still there. She was, until the door slammed shut, then she was gone. I sat down knowing that I might never see her again, a tear trickled down my face. She was gone!

The train started to gather speed as it left the train station, every child's head stuck out of a window waving rapidly until their parents faded into the distance. It was a long journey to the countryside. I munched at my stale biscuit and drank my milk to pass the time.

Suddenly, the train ground to a halt. Everyone leapt out of their seats and peered out the window. The train doors opened and we all scuttled out onto a big platform. They led us into a big hall where we sat and waited to be collected by a family. One by one children were leaving and the room was emptying. After a few hours of waiting, a lady came into the hall and came over to talk to me. Her name was Elizabeth and she said I could call her Lizzy. Then it all went quiet, was she going to take me home with her? But then she said it. I picked up my bags and made my way to the door. The lady standing there ticked off my name on the list and we went out the door and into the fresh air. I was nervous but relieved that I had been chosen.

The countryside was full of strange smells and noises and it took me a while to get used to it. We turned down the road where Lizzy lived; it was beautiful with loads of flowers and trees everywhere. I stepped inside the house. It was massive and I even had my own room upstairs.

That night I lay in bed thinking about Mum and convincing myself that she was going to be OK, but I knew she would be and I knew that I would be OK too.

Samantha Bennett (12)
St Paul's Catholic College, Burgess Hill

Theseus And The Minotaur

One year, Theseus, the greatest of the Greek heroes, said he would go and fight the monster. 'Let me go as one of the victims,' he said to his father Aegeus. 'I'll kill the Minotaur and free Greece.'

Aegeus was unsure. He remembered how others had promised to slay the beast and had ended up dead. But Theseus insisted. Soon his ship was rigged with black sails, which was the custom when Greeks were sailing to meet their doom. 'Watch out when I return,' said Theseus, 'I will hoist white sails to show that I've succeeded.'

Theseus stopped off at an island where he met a girl who fell in love with him. He did not really like her so when they were sleeping, Theseus crept onto the boat and sailed away, leaving her behind.

Theseus walked into the maze with the piece of cotton Ariadne had given him. He finally found the Minotaur. After a while he battled with the Minotaur and eventually killed it.

When he got home he found out that his dad had killed himself.

Mitch Malyon (11)
St Paul's Catholic College, Burgess Hill

Theseus And The Minotaur

There was a man called Theseus. He had a plan to go and kill the Minotaur, so that morning he set off and went to find the monster.

The first thing he had to do was sail across the sea. When he had sailed across the sea, he stopped at a small island where he met a woman. She said that if she helped him, he had to promise to marry her. Theseus agreed and the next morning they went on.

After a few more hours he finally got to where the Minotaur lived. As he was about to go down, the woman gave him a ball of string. He said, 'What's this for?'

The woman said, 'Use the string to find your way out.' So off he went.

As he got further into the cave, the more smelly it got. He finally got to the Minotaur. All he saw was dirt and this big thing that was sitting there. As the Minotaur tried to creep round, Theseus stood on a twig that snapped in half. Theseus and the Minotaur both stared at each other until it got up and then Theseus froze. Suddenly, the Minotaur's tail came sweeping down and Theseus had to dive to the ground. He stood up and stamped on its tail but it felt nothing, so Theseus jumped onto the monster. It tried to get him off its back but he hooked on for his life, made it up to its head and then stabbed its eyes so it could not see where it was. Theseus stabbed its mouth and the sword went right into its jaw and it fell. Was it dead or was it alive? Theseus went up to the body and touched it. Nothing happened, it was dead.

Theseus grabbed the string and followed it back as quickly as he could. He got to the top and the woman had gone. He did not know where, but he was pleased she had gone.

Theseus started to come back over the sea. He did not stop at the island. He soon got back to where he started. He rushed to the king and told him that he had killed the Minotaur. At first the king did not believe him, so Theseus opened his bag and pulled out the Minotaur's head. As the king stared into its eyes, he turned into stone. Theseus did not understand why he did not turn to stone. He went to ask people and they told him he had to look into its eyes for 15 seconds. Theseus told them about the king looking into its eyes and they said that he should be king because he had killed the Minotaur. So he became king.

Dave Barlow (12)
St Paul's Catholic College, Burgess Hill

The Shoot Out!

It was Monday morning in the back streets of Tooting, London. John, who is only 14 years old, had a hangover from the night before. He was supposed to be at school three hours ago. Most of the time he didn't go to school, he picked fights with other pupils skiving off school.

He started to lift himself out of bed and make his way down the stairs and approached Tooting Common. He phoned the rest of his gang who lived on Trinity Road, in the south of Tooting.

They started to come down to the common. They were discreetly carrying pistols and silenced pistols. The guns didn't need to be silenced because they were going to hold the shoot out on the bandstand in the centre of the common.

The other gang, all wearing Millwall shirts for some reason, came running down the road with knives and firearms. The two gangs took their positions and then started to fight. Some people started to throw knives at the rival gangs and others pulled their silenced pistols out and started shooting at their targets.

About 5 out of 25 people died and the number is still rising into double figures.

In the end, John's gang won. The other gang was gutted.

James Palmer (13)
St Paul's Catholic College, Burgess Hill

A Day In The Life Of Kirsten Dunst

6am - Woken up by the most annoying sound ever - the noise of a high-pitched trumpet getting faster and faster.

6.10am - Breakfast. I'm preparing myself for the film premiere of my newest film, Wimbledon.

6.30am - Bed massage. Really relaxing. Untenses all the tense muscles. This goes on for a whole hour.

7.30am - I'm going to Christina Star's wardrobe. Oh no, journalists. I have to just stand there and smile.

7.35am - Still here.

7.40am - I'm now in the limo. I'm having trouble deciding what to wear. I've been given this red, smooth book with every item of clothing Christina owns. She has some gorgeous clothes. I have narrowed it down to two dresses, either a red, silky, strapless dress with red stilettos and a red bag or a black cotton dress with glittery shoes and bag. *Help!*

8am - Here at last. I get in the lift with my two bodyguards, Alex and Trigger. Oh my word! Cristina's studio is gorgeous. It has mirrors all around and a beautiful glass floor. She shows me all the clothes and I spot it. The dress. The only dress not included in the book. It is a stunning baby-pink dress along with a matching bag and scarf. All I need now is a pair of shoes.

10am - Found a pair of baby-pink shoes and I love them. I'm now on my way to Auntie Jane's House of Hair.

10.10am - I'm going to have my hair in a twisted ponytail and clipped back with a hairpiece.

12pm - Now I'm going to get my make-up done. I'm going for the baby-pink look to match my dress.

2pm - I'm now going back to my hotel for a quick nap. I'm so tired.

5pm - Time for the film premiere. Getting out of the limo and I have been blinded by all the journalists flashing their really expensive cameras.

6.30pm - The film has just finished and by the look on everyone's faces, they liked it. Great.

Jace Petch (12)
St Paul's Catholic College, Burgess Hill

A Day In The Life Of A Dog

I woke up, it was a very bad awakening for me. It was a rainy and grim day, so not very nice and what made it worse was the noise outside. I'm not sure what it was but it sounded like a big roar. Then I heard my owner upstairs, so I went halfway up the stairs, but then he came out of his room and told me to get down. As I went downstairs I heard the loud sound again, so I barked and barked for ages, but it still didn't stop.

My owner came down with my lead and I was very excited.

As I came into the huge field, the smell hit me. It was the smell of these huge big things with horns. My owner called them cows or bulls, something like that. I ran around for a while but then I got a bit hot so I went to the shade. Before I knew it, it was time to go home.

I got home and it was time for my food, which I really didn't like. But it was food and I was hungry so I ate it. Once I'd finished my food I slept for ages because no one was in the house, but I didn't know why.

I woke up and my owner was just stepping in the door. He gave me a bone and then he played with me for a while, so I was happy. It started to get dark, I was lying on my bed and I had been for ages. My owner got up and turned everything off and closed all the doors. He was going back upstairs for the night. I was getting tired, so I got on my bed and fell asleep.

Jake Baldwin (13)
St Paul's Catholic College, Burgess Hill

Galactic War

A long time in the future there was a planet which went by the name of Kenrack. The species on this planet were the Kenrackians and they were fighting a raging war against the Dintants from Sirlock 9 from the Rincoat galaxy. This war had been going for over 8,000 light years and the raging war had now come to a climax.

The Dintants were moving in on the big, luscious rainforest planet and were ready for war. Kenrack and the Kenrackians were ready for the attack. They had mounted their laser turrets and their inton tanks and every soldier was waiting. It was the beginning of the greatest and final war, it was time.

The Dintants were moving in and then the Dintants' swoopers flew in and started hammering the laser turrets with their laser guns. Then the transporters landed and dropped thousands of these gooey, green aliens. The Kenrackians used their forest know-how to try to outflank them. They jumped out of the woods behind the Dintants and took out loads of them. One of the Dintants' bomber ships swooped in and bombed the Kenrackians, taking thousands of them out. The battle was raging on, but nobody looked like they were winning or losing. Something had to be done.

It was the Dintants who decided that they had had enough of this. One of the ships flew up out of the atmosphere and went towards the Dintants' mothership. It landed in one of the docking bays and a Dintant got out. He ran across the bay and changed ships. He got into a power bomber ship and headed back to the battle.

When he got there, he flew on top of the battle and dropped an ion bomb. It went down with a thunderous bang and wiped out everything. The power of the bomb put off the pilot and made him crash into a nearby tree. The cloud of dust disappeared and two things stood there - a Kenrackian and a Dintant. They looked at each other and drew their laser pistols out. They both fired and hit. Both were dead and that was the end of the war between the Kenrackians and the Dintants - *or was it?*

Josh Szweda (13)
St Paul's Catholic College, Burgess Hill

In-Between The Devil's Jaws

Crack! Crack! Gunshots filled the air and thick smoke was billowing around me like dense fog, swamping me, drowning me. I struggled and fought for every breath as I stumbled forward towards the trenches, the noise of the airguns now penetrating my brain. And all the time darkness was washing over me and I was drawn deeper and deeper into the pits of death.

Until suddenly, I felt as though I had really died, as though I was in paradise. *Is this what it feels like to be dead?* I wondered. It was bliss - so quiet, so peaceful and almost friendly. Then the racket started up again, like a thousand hammers all trying to break my skull and I knew I was still alive, but the enemy had come round for another attack, from a position to their advantage. Their hands would have control over me; my life depended on their mercy. They were steadily closing in, firing shots that rang out in the chilled and damp air as night drew around me like a cloak folding its creases, as if I were a person it could never leave.

Suddenly, the barrel of a shotgun was thrust into my face, rough hands shook me, and an unkempt face was plunged into my chest, clearly checking whether I was still alive, whether they would have the satisfaction of torturing me, killing me. This was my downfall, my end. As I looked upon that uniform so cruel. The one I had come to overthrow. The one that had killed innocent.

Yet I still had hope, just like a ray of sunshine on the horizon, I knew I would survive. I would save my country and live to the very end. But would the hope survive?

Beth Humphrey (13)
St Paul's Catholic College, Burgess Hill

A Day In The Lives Of Kira, Millie And Kimmy

A day in the lives of Kira, Millie and Kimmy, three teenage triplets. A day like no other in their lives. A day when their whole world is turned upside down. It was a year and a half after their younger brother, Max was born. The girls were only 7 and were at home alone with Max as their dad was at work and their mum was at the local supermarket across the road, when suddenly Max was burning up and screaming. They tried ringing Mum's mobile, but heard it on the dining room table, so Kira, currently in her slippers, ran faster than she had ever done before across the road into the supermarket. As soon as she told her mum, the basket crashed to the floor as they both ran out of the shop as fast as they could.

Once Alley (Mum) got in, she grabbed the phone and rang their dad. Whilst Kira was out, Millie had rung the hospital whilst Kimmy looked after Max. When Alley got hold of Dad, the ambulance came. They all got into the ambulance. Meanwhile, Dad turned round on the motorway and crashed into the lorry behind. He was unconscious and paramedics were racing down the motorway. They had managed to get hold of Alley and the kids and that made them more panicky, two of their family members were in serious pain. What they didn't realise was that their dad was dead. They were told the news that their brother was near death as well.

Alley took Kira, Millie and Kimmy to her mum's and rushed back to the hospital. Whilst she was at her mum's, Max made a full recovery, but still needed looking after. That put a little less pain on them all. It was the worst day of their lives.

Kayleigh Woodward (12)
St Paul's Catholic College, Burgess Hill

A Forgotten Tale Of King Arthur And Merlin

It was a sunny day in the town of Camelot. Birds were soaring through the sky. Emerald-green grass was sparkling in the sun's rays. The bushy trees in the forest were as tall as the skyscrapers in New York. Suddenly, a mysterious, swirling, purple circle appeared and Merlin and King Arthur emerged from it. Merlin was wearing violet robes with moons and stars on them, Arthur was wearing shiny steel armour that gave a very clear reflection. 'Ouch!' they spoke as they landed on the ground.

King Arthur and Merlin were time-travelling. Merlin had created a device that could teleport people as well as time-travel. They were in the year 2020 and were adventuring round Camelot in different years looking at how Camelot changed over time.

So they set off to the castle in the distance and when they got there they saw that encased in a gleaming cabinet was Excalibur, as shiny as jewellery. Slowly but carefully, Arthur grasped Excalibur and started playing with it like Star Wars' fans playing with lightsabers.

Suddenly, a loud bang erupted like a volcano as the sound of steel clashed with hard, rugged stone. The vibration of this climax dented Excalibur. King Arthur was surprised at his own strength but was worried because he had just broken a sword as powerful and magical as Harry Potter. Fortunately, Merlin was at hand and was able to use his magic to mend the sword after of couple of magic phrases and pouring a slimy green potion on it. Merlin had told Arthur that they should travel back to their own time because of what had just happened. Arthur agreed and once they were in the time portal travelling back to their time period, Arthur remembered he had taken the new Excalibur with him!

Rowan Pellegrin (13)
St Paul's Catholic College, Burgess Hill

The Day The World Died

They were tall, black and had four arms.

It was clear they were extraterrestrials, not from Earth. They made their way through the town, shooting innocent humans with the strange laser rifles they carried. Bodies were lying across roads, pavements and in shop doorways. From the planet Zargon, in another dimension, these aliens were only on Earth to kill and destroy.

With death all around him, Jimmy ran towards his home, dodging and weaving through the invaders and the people running from them. These creatures, called Zargonians, crashed and crushed. 'Everybody run!' an army officer shouted, while engaged in battle with one of the monsters.

Jimmy looked to the officer, only to see him on the ground, lifeless. In a flash, Jimmy felt a searing pain in his left leg. Looking down, he froze. The skin on his leg had burnt away, leaving him with the sight of blood, muscle and bone. He turned, to be greeted by a Zargonian. His head was covered in a black material, with eye holes. *This is it, my death,* Jimmy thought. Like many others around him, he was right. Collapsing in a heap on the ground, he took his last breath. He was dead.

The murderous monsters continued to destroy Earth. The army and police were no good, scientists couldn't work out where they came from and mankind began to become extinct.

In two months no one was left. The world had died and nobody could do anything about it. The world that took billions of years to develop, was wiped out in two months.

Alex White (13)
St Paul's Catholic College, Burgess Hill

Ernie's Bad Day

'I don't care if the company can't afford it!' Ernie was furious with his boss. He was broke, had an awful job and spent his life alone. However, he thought himself a mastermind. He fantasized about taking over the world and having his boss, Donald Parkinson, as his personal assistant. He had simply gone in there to ask for a pay rise so he could afford the basics of life, and now it looked like he would be unemployed for the rest of his life as his boss had just sacked him.

Later that day he was trying to work out how to get his job back. Although he hated being in a stuffy office in the middle of the grubby side of London with a boss as stubborn as Ernie's old mother-in-law, he needed the money and he was too stupid (or as he described it, mentally challenged) to understand what to do in another occupation.

He walked across the park and into the newsagents where he bought a newspaper and a Mars bar (as they came as a deal). He flipped to the back of the paper, dug out a pen and started the crossword. This particular crossword would win him £250,000, enough to buy him a new house and a decent suit. However, Ernie was awful at that sort of thing and way too 'mentally challenged' to work it out.

Suddenly, his ex mother-in-law came up to him, handed the astonished man a bag of chips and a piece of paper and skipped off, her overly made-up face twitching a little. She had given him the answers! He hurriedly copied it, bought a stamp and sent it off.

Nowadays, well let's just say, he doesn't need his job back.

Keri George (13)
St Paul's Catholic College, Burgess Hill

I Saw What You Did

It was a chilly, dark night and all six of them walked through the horrifyingly scary forest, leaves crunching behind them. Slowly and nervously, they walked towards the abandoned house where only a few months ago, a rejected baby had died because its family had strangely disappeared. When the police investigated, they discovered a dismembered corpse of an infant. Its missing parts were nowhere to be found. However, the six adolescents did not know this as they had come from the other side of town.

As moonlit shadows danced across the woodland floor, a cold breeze swept through the forest. Suddenly, they heard a strange noise that sounded almost like a baby's voice, 'Don't come, I know what you did.'

By this time they were all freaked because on the way down that night, they had hit something and so they had all got out of the car and seen a body, but they were so scared that they all ran hastily back to the car. But one of them, named Charlie, expressed that they should do something. Therefore, they once again got out but now the body had disappeared and there was no trace of it. So, in disbelief, they got out of there as quickly as possible.

Now they knew what the voice was talking about, but Lucy suggested it was all a big prank and they had nothing to worry about, so they all continued walking to the house.

When they got inside the door they all got goosebumps. However, one of them opened the door and they all walked in and it was dark and creaky. Charlie had realised that there was something going on in the other room, only to see that there was a little baby playing with its missing mother and father's dead bodies and it said, 'I told you, I know what you've done!' It then started eating one of the eyeballs and its head twisted 360° with an evil smile on its face.

Genn Junior Maravolo (13)
St Paul's Catholic College, Burgess Hill

Apocalypse

Jake walked down the metal staircase of the abandoned library and walked towards the blue light. With every step he took, the temperature fell.

He turned the corner and there on the floor, huddled over a book under a floating globe of light, was an old man with strange tattoos covering his skin. The man looked at Jake with red, pupil-less eyes that narrowed.

'What are you doing here?' whispered Jake.

The man just laughed, a laugh that sounded like a thousand nails on a chalkboard and mumbled words Jake couldn't understand. The tattoos glowed and Jake was thrown against the wall. Just before he passed out, blue symbols flashed before his eyes.

Ten years later

'Ladies and gentlemen, we're pleased to welcome here at the Royal Museum of Ancient Artefacts, Jake Bowen and Ben Town who have just returned from deepest Africa and recovered a magnificent statue,' announced the director of the museum.

Jake looked at the writing on the base of the statue that said: 'The one who can beat him has the mark of destruction upon his arm'. There were also ten symbols he recognised at the top as those that had flashed before his eyes when the old man knocked him out all those years ago.

'Ben, what do those symbols men at the top?' asked Jake.

'Um, Ap-oc-al-ypse, Apocalypse.'

Jake's face fell as he touched the mark on his arm and realised he was the one who had to defeat the Apocalypse!

Joe Wibberley (14)
The Grove School, St Leonards-on-Sea

It Was Never Meant To Happen

As I climbed the stairs, the high-pitched screams of the public began to worry me - the loud crying of the poor girl's family broke my heart. I continued to run up the stairs; I could no longer feel my legs. It were as if a dagger had been stuck in each one. I finally reached the top of the building - I could hear my heart pounding against my ribs.

I saw her standing there. Her eyes were red and she was crying very much. Her hands were shaking irritably fast. I felt my stomach sink. *This is my fault*, I thought, full of remorse. I walked nearer to her, very slowly, so I would not frighten her. 'Sarah,' I whispered, 'please come down.' After no response, I knew that she was aware I was standing next to her. 'Sarah?' I tried again.

'Go away now,' she said between her gritted teeth, with the most malicious voice I have ever heard. 'I *will* jump.'

For some reason, I was certain she would not. How could she? I did not mean to do what I did. It was an accident.

Her feet grew nearer and nearer to the edge of the building. Beads of sweat fell from my forehead and smacked the ground.

She jumped. She jumped and it was all my fault.

Amrou Al-Kadhi (15)
The Harrodian School, London

Wings Of Fire

Nadia put her finger to her nose and inhaled the white powder, closing her eyes to savour the sensation. Her body felt numb and yet full of energy; she felt as if she were on fire, beautiful and radiant. She felt as though she had become a goddess. Next to her Kerry sat laughing, her dark curls bouncing up and down with the motion of her body.

They sat, side by side on the grand bed, committing suicide. All their lives, everything that had ever happened to them, everything amounted up to this resolution, an idea of pure genius and evil. All their pain, it had all been worth it. *Worth her,* Nadia thought silently.

They had found each other not so long ago. Nadia had been raped. This place that was when Kerry came to her, in the black streets of Los Angeles - the one true angel had come to her. That was all in the past.

'What happens now?' asked Kerry as she fell back onto the bed. Her words came slowly as if she was having difficulty speaking.

'I take you away,' answered Nadia and pulled Kerry into a tight embrace.

'Where to?'

'The City of Angels.'

'Will you walk?' She sounded distant, her body limp. Dead.

'No, I'll fly. We'll fly.'

Zai Dinassylova (15)
The Harrodian School, London

Betrayal

Cole held his wife, Julienne, close for the last dance of their first anniversary party. The guests were slowly filing out until it was only Julienne and Cole left in the beautiful garden of their two-storey home. They stopped dancing and Cole led Julienne into the living room. 'I love you,' he whispered.

Julienne felt like she was in a world of bliss. The day Cole had asked for her hand in marriage was the day when all of Julienne's dreams came true. Cole pulled her closer and locked her in a tight embrace. Julienne relaxed into his arms. She thought about how lucky she was to have a husband who loved her so dearly, who she cherished so much she could recognise his heartbeats. 'I love you t ...' Julienne felt a stab of pain run through her side. She fell back in Cole's arms. He let go of her and allowed her to collapse to the floor. Julienne looked up in surprise and in Cole's hand, saw a bloodstained knife, the very knife that had dug into her flesh.

'I'm sorry,' Cole said. 'If there was any other way, I'd never have hurt you. But this was the only way I could get your father's money. With you dead, he won't last long. If you stayed alive, he would've left everything to you. I couldn't let that happen.'

Julienne's heart sank. 'If you wanted money, you could've asked me. I would've given my life for you.'

'And that's exactly what you've done.'

Julienne felt her heartbeats slow. The very man who used to make her heart race was the very man who made it stop.

Farah Kassam (15)
The Harrodian School, London

A Day In The Life Of Influenza!

9am Oh, what a night! Last night I shot out of Gary's nose at 150mph. Don't worry, I made sure that I left some clones of me behind. Anyway, I went straight into the mouth of Michelle. Unfortunately, I lost one of my legs when Gary's handkerchief got in the way of it.

10.30am I woke up this morning feeling very unwell. Michelle has been pumping herself full of paracetamol because she sensed my arrival last night. I have decided to get my own back on her by making clones of myself and making her ill.

1.30pm Phew! I've just finished making 300,000,000 clones of myself and am ready to exit the left nostril in 30 seconds time. OK. 3, 2, 1 - blast-off!

1.31pm Michelle has just sneezed and I am flying through the air towards Peter. I am due to go up his nostril in five seconds time.

3.30pm Have been inside Peter for a good two hours now and don't really know what to do. I have tried some clones on him but he has a very strong immune system. It might be something to do with seniors getting free flu jabs at the surgery.

5pm Have left Peter and am settling down inside Zoe. I am just about to create some clones. The cancer inside her means that her immune system is down. This is a gold mine.

7pm Have just made clones and am absolutely exhausted after such an exciting day. I am going to sleep in the sinuses early. Being the flu is very busy work.

Eleanor Wallace (13)
Wareham Middle School, Wareham